PARTIAL HOSPITALIZATION
FOR THE MENTALLY ILL

A Study of
Programs and Problems

PUBLICATIONS
OF THE
JOINT INFORMATION SERVICE

The Community Mental Health Center: An Interim Appraisal, by Raymond M. Glasscote, M.A., James N. Sussex, M.D., Elaine Cumming, Ph.D., and Lauren H. Smith, M.D. 1969.

The Treatment of Alcoholism: A Study of Programs and Problems, by Raymond M. Glasscote, M.A., Thomas F. A. Plaut, Ph.D., Donald W. Hammersley, M.D., Francis J. O'Neill, M.D., Morris E. Chafetz, M.D., and Elaine Cumming, Ph.D. 1967.

Health Insurance for Mental Illness, by Patricia L. Scheidemandel, Charles K. Kanno, and Raymond M. Glasscote. 1968.

Approaches to the Care of Long-Term Mental Patients, by Helen Padula, M.S.W., Raymond M. Glasscote, M.A., and Elaine Cumming, Ph.D. 1968.

The Psychiatric Emergency: A Study of Patterns of Service, by Raymond M. Glasscote, M.A., Elaine Cumming, Ph.D., Donald W. Hammersley, M.D., Lucy D. Ozarin, M.D., and Lauren H. Smith, M.D. 1966.

General Hospital Psychiatric Units: A National Survey, by Raymond M. Glasscote and Charles K. Kanno. 1965.

Fifteen Indices: An Aid in Reviewing State and Local Mental Health and Hospital Programs. 1968 edition.

Private Psychiatric Hospitals: A National Survey, by Charles K. Kanno and Raymond M. Glasscote. 1966.

The Community Mental Health Center: An Analysis of Existing Models, by Raymond M. Glasscote, M.A., David Sanders, M.D., M.P.H., H. M. Forstenzer, M.S., and A. R. Foley, M.D. 1964.

PARTIAL HOSPITALIZATION FOR THE MENTALLY ILL

A Study of Programs and Problems

RAYMOND M. GLASSCOTE, M.A.
Chief, Joint Information Service

ALAN M. KRAFT, M.D.
Chairman, Department of Psychiatry,
Albany Medical College

SIDNEY M. GLASSMAN, Ph.D.
Chief of Psychology,
Fort Logan Mental Health Center

WILLIAM W. JEPSON, M.D.
Chief, Psychiatry,
Hennepin County General Hospital,
Minneapolis

31643

A publication of
THE JOINT INFORMATION SERVICE
of the
AMERICAN PSYCHIATRIC ASSOCIATION
and the
NATIONAL ASSOCIATION FOR MENTAL HEALTH

WASHINGTON, D. C., 1969

Manufactured by GARAMOND/PRIDEMARK PRESS, BALTIMORE

THE JOINT INFORMATION SERVICE

of the AMERICAN PSYCHIATRIC ASSOCIATION

and the NATIONAL ASSOCIATION FOR MENTAL HEALTH

Additional copies of this publication are available from THE JOINT INFORMATION SERVICE, 1700 18th Street, N.W., Washington, D. C. 20009 (cloth, $6, paper, $4; discounts for quantity purchases).

This book results from an investigation carried out as a joint undertaking of the Joint Information Service and the National Institute of Mental Health. Approximately three quarters of the funds for the project were furnished under Public Health Service Contract No. PH–43–67–1322; the balance came from the budget of the Joint Information Service.

Acknowledgments

The authors express their appreciation to Dr. Lucy Ozarin of the National Institute of Mental Health, who served as project officer and accompanied us on our visits to nine of the twelve facilities described herein. She made many useful and helpful suggestions. We are greatly indebted to Dr. Alan I. Levenson, who accompanied us on certain visits and who provided encouragement to us throughout the project. Dr. Alan Levine and Dr. Jon E. Gudeman also participated in the field work. The Joint Information Service staff provided the customary superb support and assistance. Most of all we are in the debt of the programs we visited, all of which took great pains to provide extensive orientation material and to arrange the visits to meet our needs.

CONTENTS

I. Introduction

THE PRACTICE OF providing care to the seriously mentally ill only during the daytime rather than around the clock began in Russia, in the early 1930's. It is said to have come about not so much from theoretical and philosophical persuasions as from financial expediency: there simply were not sufficient funds to build additional hospitals.

Although a program with many of the attributes of the day hospital was operated at Adams House in Boston starting in 1935,* it appears that the first North American day hospital to be situated within a traditional hospital was that established in 1946 by the late Dr. D. Ewen Cameron at Allen Memorial Institute in Montreal. The following year Dr. Cameron put forward his persuasion† that the day hospital could manage all types of patients, with the major advantage of allowing the patient to be treated in the context of his family. He observed that psychiatric units in general hospitals were handicapped by three traditional medical characteristics: *a*) a hospital is a place to go to bed, *b*) a patient stays until he is well, and *c*) only the patient is treated.

A decade later, Dr. Cameron was still very nearly alone as an advocate of the advantages of part-time hospitalization. In 1956 he expanded on his original thesis that the traditional medical model is not suitable for psychiatric patients and set forth some guidelines for operating a day hospital.‡ Specifically, *a*) the unit should not hold more than twenty patients, *b*) patients should be selected in terms of appropriate kinds of behavior, and *c*) all forms of treatment available in inpatient facilities could be applied to day care.

Dr. Cameron also identified certain problems that may plague the day hospital. Some patients may find it difficult to consider the day hospital "a real hospital," and it may be difficult to get patients living at any distance from the hospital to attend.

---

*W. E. Barton: *Administration in Psychiatry*. Charles C. Thomas, Springfield, Ill., 1962, pp. 167-170.

†D. E. Cameron: "The Day Hospital: Experimental Form of Hospitalization for Patients," *Modern Hospital* 69:60-62, September 1947.

‡D. E. Cameron: "The Day Hospital," in A. E. Bennett *et al., The Practice of Psychiatry in General Hospitals.* University of California Press, Berkeley and Los Angeles, 1956, pp. 134-150.

1

IN 1958 the American Psychiatric Association sponsored a day hospital conference,* at which the similarities and differences among the programs represented were discussed. The psychiatrists were said to differ in the extent to which they used somatic treatments, but they agreed on the therapeutic value of supervised work, play, and socialization provided in day care programs. All of the programs emphasized a fully programmed day, typically from 9 a.m. to 4 p.m., Monday through Friday. There was considerable variation among them in terms of the kind of personnel assigned. Most of the programs were housed in whatever premises they could get rather than in anything designed specifically for a day program. And for the most part they were treating two types of patients: those who had been inpatients and were placed in the day hospital for a transitional period prior to discharge, and those who were assigned to the day center as an alternative to inpatient care.

The conferees identified two major problems: legal responsibility and cost. Actually, none of the participants had encountered any legal difficulties, but they were concerned that day programs theoretically assume a considerable risk. As for the cost, it was agreed that while the per diem expenses of day hospitals were much higher than those of state mental hospitals, the total treatment for the entire episode of illness was less expensive.

These recommendations were adopted:

• Each state department of mental hygiene should take up the concept of the day hospital "as an experimental substitute" for new or expanded hospital buildings.

• Every building then being planned should incorporate a day center.

• Psychiatric training centers should incorporate day hospital training for residents, medical students, and interns.

• In planning psychiatric facilities for parts of the country that have none, a day hospital should be considered in preference to inpatient services.

• Local medical societies should be included in the planning and operation of day hospitals.

Since the proceedings reflect that there were known to be only eight day hospitals in the United States, it appears that this new treatment arrangement had been adopted at a leisurely pace. Nonetheless, the outlook of the conferees was optimistic. They were convinced that the rising cost of hospital construction would force a search for new and less expensive methods, and that new methods of treatment and new kinds of professional skills were becoming increasingly available.

---

*Proceedings, 1958 Day Hospital Conference. American Psychiatric Association, Washington, D. C., 1958.

I N 1963 the National Institute of Mental Health carried out a national survey* intended to identify day and night treatment programs and to determine the number of patients they were currently seeing. With a 95 percent response, a total of 141 programs were identified in 114 facilities. They were seeing 2909 patients in day services and 671 patients in day-night services. The optimism of the APA conferees was confirmed.

In 1968, the Joint Information Service carried out a survey intended principally to identify programs suitable for the field study reported herein. An NIMH list, updated to 1965, and augmented by the Joint Information Service, was used. With an 82 percent response, this survey identified 141 facilities with a total of 185 partial hospitalization programs. Assuming that the 36 nonrespondents had patient loads at the same rate as the 141 respondents, these programs had an active caseload early in 1968 of approximately 8500.

It seems certain that additional partial hospitalization programs have been established since 1965, and probably there are still other earlier programs that were identified neither by the NIMH nor the Joint Information Service surveys. Furthermore, the scores of federally assisted community mental health centers that will begin operating in the near future will all be required to provide at least day care for the mentally ill.

And so, after a very slow start in the dozen years after Dr. Cameron established his program in Montreal, the pace finally accelerated. One could conclude that the advantages of partial hospitalization over full-time hospitalization have been accepted by the mental health professions, and that partial hospitalization has become a major intensity of treatment.

B UT HAS IT? The coin has another side. The country is known to have at least 1200 facilities that provide psychiatric inpatient care. Even if we assume that there are in actuality perhaps half again as many facilities providing partial hospitalization programs as we have thus far identified, the number would be about 265. Consequently, for every inpatient facility that provides some form of partial hospitalization program, there are almost four that provide none at all.†

---

*M. Conwell *et al.:* "The First National Survey of Psychiatric Day-Night Services," in R. Epps and L. Hanes (eds.), *Day Care of Psychiatric Patients.* Charles C. Thomas, Springfield, Ill., 1964, pp. 106-115.

†This comparison would assume that all partial hospitalization programs are operated within inpatient facilities. The evidence suggests that this is in fact true of the substantial majority.

The contrast is far more striking when we consider the relative numbers of patients. Assuming once more that there are half again as many partial hospitalization programs as our survey identified, we can project a total active caseload early in 1968 of 12,250 patients. In state mental hospitals, general hospital psychiatric units, Veterans Administration psychiatric services, and private psychiatric hospitals there were approximately 500,000 inpatients on any given day during the same period. Thus, for every person being cared for in partial hospitalization, there appear to be *more than forty* who are confined to hospitals as inpatients. From this vantage point, it appears that most of the growth of partial hospitalization is yet to come.

WHAT IS MORE, existing programs, if we can judge by the twelve that were visited in the course of this study, have a variety of problems of definition, relationship, and program for which solutions are yet to be found. These problems were inherent more in the wider problems of mental health services (and all helping services) and in the newness of the partial hospitalization concept than in the internal characteristics of the programs, which as a group were of high quality. They were making commendable efforts to provide a useful and successful service to their clients and to the community, and they showed much comparability in program content and therapeutic philosophy.

In the face of an imputed absolute shortage of community-based mental health services, it may sound surprising that the greatest problem facing most of these programs was that of getting and keeping patients. Nine of the twelve programs had chronic problems in maintaining an adequate stream of referrals, and most had a problem with large numbers of dropouts, particularly within the first few days of treatment. There were also problems of relationships with relatives, of transportation, and of financing, among others.

II. The Purpose and the Method of This Study

THE JOINT INFORMATION SERVICE and the National Institute of Mental Health in 1967 undertook a joint contract calling for the Joint Information Service to carry out a series of studies of aspects of community-based mental health services. The studies have as their purpose to examine existing services in order to identify their strengths and successes, as well as their weaknesses and their problems, in the hope thereby that other programs less far along in development can avoid some of the difficulties that these early-established programs have experienced. Partial hospitalization, as a service required to be provided in every federally supported community mental health center, was agreed upon as the second in the series.

In retrospect, it appears that we would have benefited from a national survey to obtain considerable detail about a large number of programs from which to select a few for intensive study. However, such an effort was outside the scope of our contract and would have required far more time than was available. Furthermore, the authors, the Joint Information Service staff and consultants, and NIMH personnel already knew of a number of partial hospitalization programs that appeared to be operating successfully. Consequently, the majority of the twelve programs studied were chosen on the basis of our personal acquaintance with them. At the same time, in an attempt to identify any additional programs that might warrant inclusion, the Joint Information Service sent a brief identifying questionnaire to a large number of facilities. Only one was chosen for inclusion, although there were a number of others that might have been included if we had not already identified suitable examples having the required characteristics (such as operating auspices, size, and location).

Each facility selected for study was asked to complete a lengthy questionnaire whose answers would orient the authors in advance of their visits. All of the site visits were made during the first four months of 1968. During our visits we interviewed a number of staff members, including all or substantially all of the professional staff in most of the facilities.

5

In May 1968 the Joint Information Service brought together one or more representatives of each program (17 persons representing 12 facilities) for a conference with the survey team, plus representatives of the American Psychiatric Association and the National Institute of Mental Health. An agenda based on the issues and problems that the authors had discerned during their visits was considered during a two-day period.

Thereafter descriptions of the individual facilities were prepared and then submitted to the facilities with the request that they check for accuracy and completeness, and each did so.

This monograph is a distillation of the identifying survey, the written material prepared for us by the twelve facilities we visited, the trip reports of the authors, the transcript of the conference, a review of the literature of partial hospitalization, and many facts and impressions gathered in conversations over the past year. While authorship is ascribed to the members of the site visit team, we are completely in the debt of the many people who gave us generous access to their knowledge and experience.

III. Definitions

PARTIAL HOSPITALIZATION, if a cumbersome and strange-sounding term, has the advantage of being an apt generic term to embrace day, night, evening, and weekend care—or treatment, or center, or service, or hospital. But beyond this generic term, definition breaks down completely. There are various purposes, emphases, and clienteles among partial hospitalization programs, but there is no uniform terminology to denote the differences.

Some of the persons we interviewed expressed the wish that the mental health professions in the United States would adopt the English practice of delineating day programs as either *day hospital* or *day care*. The British psychiatrist Dr. Douglas H. Bennett explains the difference as it obtains in England: a day hospital is a program in which every form of treatment that could be provided in a psychiatric hospital is available, while a day center is independent of a hospital and provides social and occupational services plus limited medical supervision.*

But in this country, no uniform terminology is in use except within the Veterans Administration. The Veterans Administration has come to place great emphasis on day programs of two kinds. Its *day hospitals* are located within the psychiatric services of its general hospitals; their patients are for the most part acutely ill, and the goal is to return them to essentially independent and productive lives in the community. Its second type of day program, attached to its outpatient clinics, is called *day treatment centers*—curiously, in terms of their primary goal of maintaining and rehabilitating chronic patients.

Beyond this, partial hospitalization programs appear to go by any number of different names. Except for the fact that there can be legal and financial considerations surrounding the use of the term *hospital,* we could find little to choose among them. Possibly it would be useful

---

*D. H. Bennett: "British Day Hospitals," in R. Epps and L. Hanes (eds.), *Day Care of Psychiatric Patients.* Charles C. Thomas, Springfield, Ill., 1964, pp. 116-126.

to propose that from the generic term *partial hospitalization* we might proceed to generic terms of *day program, night program, evening program,* and *weekend program* and to propose that persons being seen in them are on day, night, evening, or weekend status. But an attempt to discern real differences in meaning between *care* vs. *treatment,* or *center* vs. *hospital,* appears, at this stage, to be either wishful thinking or mere semantics.

It is important to recognize that day treatment may denote either *a*) a service unit or element, or *b*) merely a patient status. The latter would be the case when the day patients come into the inpatient service and join in the program taking place there.

IV. Characteristics of Partial Hospitalization Services

E VEN THOUGH we assume that there are more partial hospitalization services than our 1968 survey identified, we have reason to believe that the 141 "in scope" respondents comprise a large majority of the total group. The data furnished by them can serve to put the characteristics of partial hospitalization programs into perspective.

Our survey list contained 202 facilities, including 174 known to the National Institute of Mental Health, seven visited by the authors that were not on the NIMH list, and 21 others identified through a literature search and from material furnished by the Veterans Administration.

Because our purpose in making the survey was primarily to identify additional candidates for field study, we discontinued our effort when the time had come that further responses would not be useful in this respect. Consequently, the response was only 82 percent (166 facilities). Twenty-three from the NIMH list and two from the Veterans Administration list were "out of scope"; i.e., either they had no partial hospitalization program or they had discontinued it.

Because the Veterans Administration is a unified system and has placed particular emphasis on partial hospitalization, with patient loads considerably larger than those under other auspices, its programs are reported separately. The responses were as follows:

	Respondents	Non-respondents
37 Veterans Administration programs	29	8
140 other programs	112	28
	141	36

Within the 141 in-scope facilities responding, there were:

    139 day programs
     18 evening programs
     24 night programs
      4 weekend programs
    ───
    185

9

By combinations of program within facilities, the breakdown was:

  103 day programs only
   16 day/night programs
   12 day/evening programs
    4 day/evening/night programs
    2 day/night/weekend programs
    1 night program only
    1 evening/night program
    1 day/weekend program
    1 day/evening/weekend program
  141

The questionnaire asked that the number of persons seen in each of the partial hospitalization programs be indicated for a one-week period in the first half of 1968. These figures were furnished by 163 of the 185 programs, coming to a total of 6342 persons, or an average of 39 per program.

TABLE I

PARTIAL HOSPITALIZATION PROGRAMS BY AUSPICE
AND TYPE OF SERVICE, 141 FACILITIES

	No. re-sponding	No. providing data on patients	Total no. of patients	Average no. of patients	Range of patients
A. DAY PROGRAMS					
Veterans Administration	29	25	2510	100	25-225
State mental hospitals	45	43	1527	36	2-207
State-operated clinics or centers	11	9	470	52	6-145
University teaching programs	8	8	93	12	2- 24
Private psychiatric hospitals	8	7	186	27	1- 80
County-operated facilities	4	2	77		
Community mental health centers	8	6	191	32	16-100
Public general hospitals	3	3	94	31	13- 51
Voluntary general hospitals	7	7	86	12	1- 27
Other nonprofit	10	10	292	29	5- 80
Others	6	5	245	49	20-107
TOTAL	139	125	5771		
B. NIGHT PROGRAMS					
Veterans Administration	1	0			
State mental hospitals	9	8	114	14	2- 30
State-operated clinic or center	1	1	20		
University teaching program	1	1	2		
Private psychiatric hospitals	2	2	4		
County-operated facilities	3	2	57		
Community mental health centers	2	2	7		
Public general hospital	1	1	3		
Voluntary general hospitals	2	2	19		
Other nonprofit	1	1	10		
Other	1	1	8		
TOTAL	24	21	244		

TABLE I — Continued
PARTIAL HOSPITALIZATION PROGRAMS BY AUSPICE
AND TYPE OF SERVICE, 141 FACILITIES

	No. re-sponding	No. providing data on patients	Total no. of patients	Average no. of patients	Range of patients
C. EVENING PROGRAMS					
Veterans Administration	4	2	20	10	
State mental hospitals	7	6	162	27	8- 80
County-operated facility	1	1	8		
Community mental health centers	4	3	68	23	2- 50
Public general hospital	1	1	22		
Voluntary general hospital	1	1	2		
TOTAL	18	14	282		
D. WEEKEND PROGRAMS					
State mental hospital	1	1	11		
University teaching program	1	1	2		
County-operated facility	1	0			
Public general hospital	1	1	32		
TOTAL	4	3	45		

Twenty-seven Veterans Administration programs comprised only 17 percent of the facilities reporting the number of patients, but they had 40 percent of all the patients—2530 out of 6342.

The breakdown of programs by auspice and type of service is given in Table I.

If we assume that those programs not reporting the number of patients had patients at the same rate as those which did report the number, then in early 1968 the total caseloads of responding facilities would have been 6415 day patients, 290 night patients, 360 evening patients, and 60 weekend patients.

In terms of the number of patients seen in each program, approximately one fifth of the day programs had ten or less patients. Many of these appear to consist more of an informal arrangement for occasional patients to come in and spend the day on the inpatient service than of a formal and distinct day program. More than half of the programs (54 percent) had 30 or fewer day patients, and 70 percent had 50 or less (see Table II).

TABLE II
NUMBER OF PATIENTS SEEN, 125 DAY PROGRAMS

No. of active cases in day program	Veterans Administration	All others	Total no. of programs	Percent	Cumulative percent
5 or less		11	11	9	
6-10		12	12	10	18
11-15		11	11	9	27
16-20		13	13	10	38
21-25	2	11	13	10	48
26-30		7	7	6	54
31-40	1	9	10	8	62
41-50	3	7	10	8	70
51-75	5	10	15	12	82
76-100	6	6	12	10	91
101-150	3	2	5	4	95
151-200	4		4	3	98
More than 200	1	1	2	2	100

Only four of the night programs had more than 20 patients. Specifically:

Number of patients in night program	Number of programs
5 or less	8
6-10	4
11-15	3
16-20	2
26-30	4

There were only three evening programs that reported more than 25 patients. Specifically:

Number of patients in evening program	Veterans Administration	All others	Total no. of programs
5 or less		2	2
6-10		2	2
11-15	1	1	2
16-20		3	3
21-25		2	2
46-50	1	1	2
More than 50		1	1

Among the three weekend programs, one had 32 patients; another had 11, and another had two.

Geographically, there were no striking differences. Of all partial hospitalization programs combined, there were 44 in the Northeast, 25 in the South, 38 in North Central states, 33 in Western states. The two most populous states, California and New York, had the largest number of partial hospitalization programs—19 and 13. The only other states having ten or more were Ohio (12), Pennsylvania (11), and Massachusetts (10).

These data unfortunately cannot be compared directly with the data obtained by the National Institute of Mental Health in its 1963 survey, since a facility-by-facility breakdown was not available to us. The two surveys differ not only in that a larger number of facilities existed in 1968 but probably also in terms of particular respondents. The reader may be interested, as a general comparison, to know that in 1963 there were 19 Veterans Administration day programs reporting a total of 897 patients seen in a week, an average of 47 per program, while in 1968 we found 25 Veterans Administration day programs reporting a total of 2510 patients seen in a week, an average of 100 per program. Among all the other facilities, the 1963 survey found 122 partial hospitalization programs in 95 facilities, seeing a total of 2683 patients, or an average of 28 per facility; the 1968 survey found 151 partial hospitalization programs in 99 facilities, seeing an estimated total of 4218 patients, or an average of 43 per facility. Assuming once more that both the 1963 and the 1968 surveys identified a large majority of all partial hospitalization programs, we can conclude not only that the number of programs has increased but also that the caseload per program has increased substantially.

Once again, however, it seems appropriate to point out that all of these patients combined comprise a tiny fraction of the persons who were inpatients at this same time.

V. The Uses of Day Programs

D AY HOSPITALS can and do serve various kinds of patients, in programs aimed toward a variety of goals, including particularly:

- As an alternative to inpatient treatment
- As a transitional facility
- As a locus for intermediate-term rehabilitation of persons who have social and vocational deficits resulting from or related to mental illness
- As a service for patients so seriously impaired that, but for the support and maintenance of the day program, long-term hospitalization would be required.

Among these alternatives some may feel that the emphasis and goal smack more of *rehabilitation* than of *treatment* in the customary sense, but this seems an inappropriate distinction, since rehabilitation ought properly to be one of the main emphases of programs that purport to serve the seriously mentally ill.

There were at least occasional examples of each of these purposes in the majority of the twelve programs we visited. Only the Fort Logan Mental Health Center appeared by design to routinely incorporate all four purposes in its day program (and even there, a strong belief prevailed in the ultimate rehabilitation potential of substantially all patients).

Four of the programs could be said to combine two of the purposes listed above. Three of these admitted some patients to day status as an alternative to inpatient admission and transferred others from inpatient to day status in order to provide a transition between inpatient care and release from the hospital. The fourth combined intermediate-term rehabilitation with maintenance and support of persons with long histories of severe mental illness.

The majority of programs—seven of the twelve—saw their primary and substantially only goal as serving as an alternative to inpatient treatment.

14

Alternative to inpatient admission

Two decades ago, when a few adherents of day hospitals were enthusiastically promoting their possibilities, there was some anticipation that this new intensity of treatment might eliminate the need for inpatient services. Today that viewpoint seems to be regarded as overly ambitious and unrealistic. While most persons familiar with day programs appear to feel that they provide an appropriate *alternative* to inpatient care for many persons, we encountered none who felt that they could function as an actual *substitute* for an inpatient service. (Indeed, there seemed to be some evidence that an important ingredient for the success of day hospitals is immediate accessibility of inpatient service for the agitated patient who requires temporary 24-hour care.)

One major study of the use of the day hospital as a substitute for inpatient treatment has been made, at the Westchester Square Day Hospital, now incorporated into the Sound View-Throgs Neck Community Mental Health Center in the Bronx, New York (see p. 45). Through a procedure of randomly assigning to the day hospital persons already evaluated as requiring inpatient care, it was found that with moderate screening and with inpatient facilities readily available to "board" patients as required, a substantial majority of mentally ill persons could be successfully treated on day status. It is important to note that the richness of professional staff was considerably greater than is possible in most facilities, and also that the staff were occasionally pushed to extreme and nerve-racking measures in order to maintain certain of the patients in the program.

Everyone we talked with agreed that there are some mentally disturbed persons who require inpatient treatment, principally those with suicidal behavior, occasional persons likely to harm others, patients so agitated and disordered as to require heavy medication to reduce symptoms, and those too confused or disoriented to travel to the program or to benefit from it. Thus, taking into account not only the circumstances of the patient but also the need to use professional time efficiently and to avoid intolerable stress on the staff, an inpatient service seems not only necessary but a much more suitable place than a day hospital for certain relatively small categories of patients. Beyond these particular situations, there is substantial evidence that most of the persons traditionally admitted to 24-hour hospitalization can be successfully treated on day status, provided the necessary environmental supports are available outside the program.

Controlled studies are unfortunately scarce (as in every other aspect of the mental health field). Among the few reported in the literature, an early one, done by Dr. Else Kris, in 1958, at the Manhattan After-care Clinic in New York City,* is interesting, although it suffers from the small number of subjects. Seventeen patients showing severe psychotic relapse were treated in the day hospital while ten others were rehospitalized in a state mental hospital. Improvement was measured by using the Wittenborn Rating Scale both at the time of admission and at the time of discharge. All of the day patients were released from the program after periods ranging from two to six weeks, and still remained in the community three years later when the findings were published; by comparison, eight of the ten control patients had remained hospitalized during that three-year period.

At about the same time, the Bristol Day Hospital in England began to specialize in day treatment of neurosis, mainly depressive and anxiety states.† Thirty-eight neurotic day patients were matched with 38 neurotic inpatients in terms of age, illness, and length of stay. No significant difference was found in the incidence of recovery or in social adjustment following treatment. Consequently, the authors conclude, since there is no clinical advantage to hospitalization of neurotics, the economic advantages of day treatment ought to become the determinant of where they will be treated.

The California Department of Mental Hygiene in the early 1960's established freestanding day treatment centers in San Francisco, Los Angeles, and San Diego, for the purpose of providing service that would eliminate the need to send patients to state hospitals. A report of the first year's operation at the San Diego program‡ indicated that 49 of 72 patients discharged, or 69 percent, were "rated as improved and showed increased integration in their family, social, and vocational spheres of adjustment."

The day hospital at San Mateo (California) Mental Health Services reports approximately the same improvement rate.§ Of 151 patients admitted during 1966, 101, or 67 percent, "successfully completed" the treatment, which is to say that they remained in the day hospital until reasonable goals of symptom remission and/or social or vocational

---

*E. Kris: "Prevention of Rehospitalization Through Relapse Control in a Day Hospital," in M. Greenblatt et al. (eds.), Mental Patients in Transition. Charles C. Thomas, Springfield, Ill., 1961, pp. 155-162.
†S. Smith and E. Cross: "Review of 1000 Patients Treated at a Psychiatric Day Hospital," International Journal of Social Psychiatry 2:292-298, Spring 1957.
‡M. Zemlick and T. McMillan: "Day Treatment—A Study of a Year's Operation," American Journal of Orthopsychiatry 32:228-229, March 1962.
§H. R. Lamb: "Chronic Psychiatric Patients in the Day Hospital," Archives of General Psychiatry 17:615-621, November 1967.

improvement had been accomplished, and until the staff felt they were ready for discharge. No significant differences were found between the effectiveness of day treatment for patients considered to be "chronically disabled" and those considered not to be, although the former group did require a longer treatment period. According to Dr. H. Richard Lamb, "a group of patients chronically and continuously disabled by their illness for an average of 29.4 months (median, 18 months) could have treatment goals set and accomplished in a period of time averaging 14.8 weeks (median, 17 weeks) in a community mental health setting."

As a transitional facility

The literature search did not yield a single controlled study of the day program as a means of smoothing the patient's transition from inpatient care to release from the hospital, with the possible added advantage of shortening the inpatient stay. Several articles did, however, report successful experiences in this regard.

One of the earliest such programs was that established at the Menninger Foundation in the early 1950's. It grew out of the conviction that recovering patients need progressively less supervision and protection but at the same time may not be fully equipped to make an abrupt change from full hospitalization to outpatient status.*

The day care program at the McLean Hospital Rehabilitation Center was developed as a result of "the staff's realization that many patients could return to the community earlier if they could continue to use some of our facilities some of the time."†

The Lafayette Clinic in Detroit developed a day hospital program considered to be "the final step in hospital care," where a patient is placed as he continues to improve, especially in his capacity for responsibility and independence.‡

We are personally acquainted with facilities that reduced the number of beds precisely in order to have space to create a day program, among them the Massachusetts Mental Health Center, Worcester State Hospital, Hennepin County General Hospital in Minneapolis, and Denver General Hospital. In the Denver program, beds were reduced from 32 to 16 in order to make room for a day program, to which the

*M. Law: "All Therapeutic Activities Available to Day Patients," *Mental Hospitals* 4:7, February 1953.

†F. De Marneffe and J. Prekup: "The McLean Hospital Rehabilitation Center," *Mental Hospitals* 13:410-413, August 1962.

‡E. Rubin: "The Lafayette Clinic's Broad-Scale Rehabilitation Service," *Mental Hospitals* 14:383-385, July 1963.

majority of inpatients are transferred within a very few days following admission. Both in the Denver and in the Minneapolis programs the day hospital is seen as an important factor in their having been able simultaneously a) to shorten the inpatient stay, b) to reduce considerably the transfer rate to the state hospital, and c) to reduce their own inpatient readmission rate. Both of these facilities, despite reducing the number of beds, actually increased the total availability of intensive care, since the day hospital can accommodate more persons than did the beds that were removed.

The Massachusetts Mental Health Center was one of the first facilities to establish a formal day hospital service, which has been fully described in one of the very few books on partial hospitalization.* But in addition to the formal program, a transitional day hospital service developed almost spontaneously.† The patients in one of the acute treatment units began gradually to spend time away from the hospital, some going home at night, others going to work during the day. As this trend progressed, the staff removed all of the beds from one of the two wards and converted it into a day care center, adding some extra beds to the other ward so that it could function as a dormitory. Group meetings led by ward personnel were initiated "to facilitate therapeutic interaction." In its early stages the program met resistance both from patients and from staff members, but came to be enthusiastically accepted as evidence accumulated of the usefulness of the groups.

The day hospital at Hennepin County General Hospital came about as the result of a summertime shortage of nurses on an open convalescent ward that was operated as a therapeutic community. In the face of the nursing shortage, the ward was simply shut down at night; thus, a day hospital was born.

Most of these day programs with strong emphasis on transitional support appear to be more or less integrated with inpatient services. One of the authors, writing of Fort Logan Mental Health Center,‡ describes such an integrated program, which admits many persons directly to day status and also transfers large numbers of inpatients to day status. He puts forward as the advantages of a program integrated in this fashion:

---

*B. Kramer: *Day Hospital—A Study of Partial Hospitalization in Psychiatry.* Grune and Stratton, New York, 1962.
†L. Grinspoon et al.: "A Day Care Program on an Inpatient Service," *Mental Hospitals* 14:259-264, May 1963.
‡A. Kraft: "Day Hospital Services as Part of an Integrated Psychiatric Treatment Program," in R. Epps and L. Hanes (eds.), *Day Care of Psychiatric Patients.* Charles C. Thomas, Springfield, Ill., 1964, pp. 79-90.

• that the patient continues working with the same staff, whatever the status of care he happens to be in;

• that all patients needing treatment are referred to the same treatment facility;

• that there is minimal administrative work involved in transferring patients from the one status to the other;

• that 24-hour patients learn from the generally healthier day patients, while the day patients in turn learn to assume responsibility for others.

As a means of rehabilitating the long-term patient

The term rehabilitation is used in the present context to connote all of those efforts that attempt to prevent or erase the social and vocational deficits that so commonly result from or are corollary to serious mental illness. In general, we use the term in the same sense that public health professionals use the term *tertiary prevention*.

Perhaps the time has come, as more and more mental illness services are being established in local communities, to place a major emphasis on rehabilitation. Admittedly, it is not an important consideration for some patients—for example, many of the persons with acute depressive reactions, who may well have had adequate work and family relationships prior to the onset of illness and will be capable of picking up on them when the depression has lifted. But many of the seriously mentally ill, particularly schizophrenics, become hospitalized perhaps more as a result of their inadequate social and vocational capabilities than because of the illness itself. Many of them have spotty employment records, poor instrumental skills, even poorer psychosocial skills, and turbulent family relationships. For such persons a rehabilitation emphasis is of particular importance. These rehabilitative efforts can take place not only within psychiatric facilities, but, perhaps even more usefully, in such outside settings as sheltered workshops, job training projects, social clubs, and halfway houses.

All of the twelve programs we visited provided at least some activity that could be considered rehabilitative—paid work, made available either within the program or on the outside, vocational assessment, arrangements for job training, job finding, residential placements, etc.— and some were doing several of these activities, as indicated in the individual program descriptions. Only the Hawaii Convalescent Center provided for the majority of patients a sheltered work-focused program within its own physical plant, with the goal of inculcating both the instrumental and the psychosocial skills needed to acquire and maintain a job. This program emphasis seems a logical one in view of the fact that substantially all of the patients in this program come there directly from the state hospital.

Apart from the programs visited during this study, we know of a number of facilities that provide day programs with particular rehabilitation emphasis. For the most part, these are identified specifically as rehabilitation programs, rather than as mental health or psychiatric programs. They are essentially nonmedical. Examples of special work programs that include or are limited to mental patients are the Lanakila Crafts program in Honolulu, a sheltered workshop in Burlington, Vermont, a very large program in Omaha operated by Goodwill Industries, the COVE program in Everett, Washington, and Altro Work Shops, Inc. in New York City. Examples of facilities that provide special living arrangements and social programs for mentally ill persons are Fountain House in New York, Horizon House in Philadelphia, and the rehabilitation residences in Burlington and Montpelier, Vermont. Such programs are often supported largely by federal funds, through the state Division of Vocational Rehabilitation.

Maintenance of long-term patients

While ostensibly the ultimate goal for all mental patients is the capability to work and live in the community at large, most professionals agree that it is not a goal attainable for all patients. Some who have long histories of mental illness, together with extreme dependency resulting from the "institutionalization" effect of prolonged hospitalization, appear to require considerable environmental support and in terms of present professional capabilities give little promise ever of attaining essentially independent functioning. Being unable to establish themselves in a social setting, they need a ready-made social group.

There is considerable evidence that many such persons can be suitably maintained in day programs operated in the local community. Some of the Hawaii Convalescent Center patients are unable to move out of the program and into employment, and for them an activity program and simple work compensated on a piecework basis are provided for unlimited periods of time.

The largest and best developed example of this type of program is seen in the Veterans Administration's day treatment programs. Many men impaired by mental illness, with work and social skills so inadequate that they would otherwise require full-time and perhaps permanent hospitalization, are maintained in the community by means of the five-day-a-week support provided by these day treatment centers. These facilities also afford the opportunity to supervise and maintain the much needed medication.

Two additional uses of the day program

As a diagnostic method. In two of the programs we visited, the day program had been effectively used as a means of diagnosing the patient's treatment needs. In one case this had happened gratuitously, as a result of having to place patients in the day program as an expedient when no inpatient beds were available. It was found that some patients responded satisfactorily while on day status, so that when a bed became available it was not necessary for them to be hospitalized.

In various facilities that provide a range of services, there is sometimes a wait both for inpatient and for outpatient treatment. If a day program is available it may well serve as an alternative that has the added advantage of permitting more extensive observation of the patient than occurs in the typical evaluative procedure. Beyond this, persons are often admitted to inpatient status precisely for diagnostic purposes; in many such instances day status might serve at least as well. At the same time it must be considered that diagnostic admissions might interfere with day hospitals that are designed to be specialized treatment settings.

As an extension of outpatient treatment. Mental health facilities have sometimes found themselves in the position of being forced to provide only outpatient service to a person thought to need inpatient care, either because he has no money or does not meet inpatient eligibility requirements. If a day program is available, it may prove useful as an intensity of treatment which, even if less than the ideal intensity for a particular patient, is considerably more intensive than outpatient treatment.

At the Veterans Administration Day Treatment Center in Brooklyn, N.Y.,* a study was made of the relative progress over an 18-month period of 33 patients in the day treatment center and a similar group of 36 patients assigned to conventional outpatient treatment. Change was appraised by the presence or absence of such events as hospitalization and employment. Ratings of psychological adjustment were made at three-month intervals, including interpersonal relations, family relations, community relations, self-concept, motivation, affective control, mood, and dependency.

---

*J. Meltzoff and R. Blumenthal: *The Day Treatment Center.* Charles C. Thomas, Springfield, Ill., 1966.

These authors found that the day treatment center patients either held their own or improved in adjustment as members of the community and in their self-concept, their degree of independence, their relations with their family, and their general mood, while the outpatients showed a decline in all of these areas. Neither group showed any improvement in interpersonal relationships or in motivation for new achievements. The authors conclude:

> The findings suggest that the day treatment center, as herein conceived and operated, is accomplishing its major objectives, and is more economical and more effective than conventional outpatient approaches in forestalling hospitalization and modifying the community adjustment patterns and clinical status of the most marginally adjusted ambulatory schizophrenics.

VI. Some Advantages and Disadvantages of Day Programs

B EFORE CONSIDERING the issues and the problems that surround day programs the authors wish to make explicit their persuasion that this intensity of treatment is in certain respects superior to inpatient treatment for many of the persons with serious mental illness. Specifically:

- It allows the patient to maintain those independent activities of which he may be capable despite his mental illness.
- It discourages the excessive dependency and dehumanization that often develop in the course of full-time hospitalization.
- It allows the patient to remain with his family, when it is therapeutically desirable for him to do so.
- Typically it offers a more active and varied therapeutic experience than most inpatient services.
- Theoretically it should be easier to staff, since there is a regular five-day workweek.
- In most cases, it should cost less than inpatient services—in some cases substantially less.
- It approximates the customary workweek, making the patient's transition to full employment easier.
- For many patients it seems to hold less social stigma than inpatient treatment.
- It causes less sexual frustration for the patient, since there is not a prolonged period of forced sexual abstinence.
- It forces the patient to continue to work through any family problems, since he has to return to them every night. In general, denial of problems is more difficult in a day program.
- It lessens the need to find explanations for nosy neighbors.
- It usually avoids interrupting welfare checks, whereas inpatient admission often stops welfare payments.
- It forces patients to be more aware of their strengths and abilities, whereas in inpatient programs they can often see only their sickness and failings.

- It makes possible part-time jobs in the evenings and on weekends.
- It makes it easier to guard against drug reactions than is possible in outpatient services.
- It makes possible a greater quantity of intensive care than can be provided in the same space by an inpatient facility.
- It reduces the "parent-child, doctor-patient" relationship characteristic of the medical model.
- It capitalizes on the capacities of the subprofessionals and the patients themselves as helping agents.
- It blends readily with nonmedical social and vocational rehabilitation programs.
- It provides a means of tapering treatment off.

A T THE SAME TIME, it must be recognized that there are disadvantages or problems inherent in day treatment. In some cases the disadvantages are essentially only "the other side of the coin." In any event, it seems suitable, for the sake of completeness, to indicate certain of the principal negatives.

- Day treatment does not remove the patient totally from the environment precipitating the disturbance, as may be temporarily desirable or necessary for some patients.
- It runs higher risks for those patients with assaultive or suicidal potential.
- It is more fatiguing for staff, not only because of the risks cited above but also because the staff find it more difficult to avoid dealing with problems the patient lives with. There is also more testing of staff by the patient to get inpatient care.
- It is easier for day patients than it is for inpatients to drop out of the program if it does not appear relevant to their needs and problems.
- It frequently presents problems of transportation and living arrangements.
- It disappoints the patient who seeks a personal therapist and individual therapy.
- It usually interferes with employment and school.
- It promotes some degree of regression, although not as much as inpatient programs, by providing an artificial, somewhat protective environment.
- It usually costs more than outpatient care.

VII. Identifying the Patient

BECAUSE OF their special circumstances, most partial hospitalization programs set some restrictions on whom they will accept. The exclusions most commonly stated are these: *a*) suicidal patients; *b*) homicidal patients; *c*) grossly agitated persons; *d*) those unable, for whatever reason, to arrange their own transportation to and from the facility; *e*) those without supportive families or a satisfactory substitute in the way of environmental support outside the program.

The programs we visited varied in their exclusions, some having only one or two, others having several. Interestingly, the homicidal patient appears to be the only type of patient categorically excluded from all of the programs. There were two or three that are willing to take the special precautions required to accept suicidal patients. Some arranged residential placement for patients without appropriate places to live, and others accepted persons living alone.

We sought throughout our visits to identify differential clinical criteria whereby it could be determined that a particular person was a better candidate for partial hospitalization than for inpatient or outpatient care, but we were unsuccessful. The criteria appeared to consist very nearly exclusively of *a*) the patient's behavior and *b*) his supportive resources outside the hospital. Assuming that he did not carry a serious threat of suicide or homicide, was not so grossly disturbed as to disrupt the program, and had something approaching an adequate place to live, most of the programs would be willing to accept him, without reference to the diagnosis or severity of pathology.

The programs did consider themselves to be, by and large, for the treatment of major morbidity, and the diagnoses of their patients reflect that this was in fact the nature of their caseloads. A very substantial majority of the patients were persons with either schizophrenia, neurotic depression, or psychotic depression.

VIII. Recruiting the Patient

M OST OF THE TWELVE programs were operating below, and in some cases substantially below, their own specified maximum capacity. This appears to be principally because most of them are not "entry points" into the treatment network but instead must rely on referrals from other services within their own facility or from outside sources.

This underutilization results principally from two causes. The less important is the fact that some day programs give the appearance of being highly selective, of wanting only the best patients, of having numerous restrictions and conditions about behavior and life circumstances. The more important is that partial hospitalization, two decades after Dr. Cameron established his program in Montreal, is still not well developed and continues to be understood only poorly by mental health professionals and referring agencies and scarcely at all by patients and their families.

We were told at the majority of programs that the staff have to drum up business periodically, both within the facility and with outside agencies. Usually the effort is successful, and referrals increase. But curiously, the result is not sustained; sooner or later referrals fall off again, and further recruitment efforts must be made.

Dr. Jack Wilder regards the problem as administrative. He said, "Unless a day hospital has some control over the point of admission, it will have a census problem, resulting in the need to make periodic swoops on the emergency room or the inpatient service. When one has some control over admissions, the situation is far more favorable."

Dr. Walter Friedman attributes the problem to negative feelings toward the day hospital by the inpatient service. "The day hospital is apt to be considered a luxury service, one that picks only the best and most communicative patients, who are willing to come on their own and have more initiative. And the inpatient staff want these patients for themselves, because they find it too depressing to work only with people who won't move." (We should add here, however, that during our visits we saw numerous patients who did not appear to be very communicative nor in other ways to resemble what is usually thought of as a "prize patient.")

Dr. Frederick Glaser suggests that the reluctance of professionals to refer to day programs is related to the fact that most such programs use group psychotherapy and other group procedures which he feels many practitioners consider inferior to individual treatment.

Dr. Gertrude Gross says that the Baltimore City Psychiatric Day Center has a regular midyear "run down" in census. "The people who are in charge of referrals sometimes simply forget what is available," she said. "We noticed that we were receiving no referrals from the two teaching hospitals in our vicinity during the months of July and August. When we looked into it, we found that the new residents who had come on duty had not been told by their supervisors about our day program."

Dr. Wilder and Dr. Werner Simon also suggest that when residents run the inpatient service they are apt to be reluctant to refer patients to the day hospital. "The resident doesn't want to surrender the patient, just when he's established a relationship, especially if the patient's improving," Dr. Wilder said.

Dr. Ethel Bonn says that Fort Logan Mental Health Center sometimes had cases in which the referring agency had already decided that the patient required inpatient care and was then annoyed to find that Fort Logan had placed the individual on day status. "This gets worked out only with a great deal of education and discussion with the referring agency," she said, "or when the referring agency opens its own day program." This points up the common problem of referring agencies and their personnel having no experience with day programs and what they can handle.

Referrals from non-mental health agencies

There were predictably few referrals to most of the twelve programs from such sources as welfare departments, schools, ministers, and the police. Referrals from such sources usually constitute a relatively small part of the caseload even of inpatient and outpatient services, since the established referral pattern is typically first to a general practitioner or to some generic medical facility. It would be expecting a very great deal of sophistication on the part of a non-mental health facility to ascertain that a client appears not only to be mentally ill but specifically to be in need of partial hospitalization, or any other particular intensity of care.

Family referrals

For many mental health facilities, family members represent a major, in some cases the largest, source of referrals. There are relatively few family referrals in the programs that we visited, presumably because they are specialized services of a kind relatively unknown to the public.

IX. Retaining the Patient

THE MOST IMPORTANT agent in the day hospital's effort to recruit a caseload is the patient himself. Substantially all admissions to day hospitals are on a voluntary basis, with the occasional exception of persons required by the courts to attend as a condition of probation. Furthermore, the day hospital cannot always convert the voluntary admission to an involuntary one in the way that most inpatient services are able to do when they feel it necessary for his own safety to retain a patient who wants to leave.

There are two problems: to convince the patient that it is in his interest to enter the program, and, once he has done so, that it is in his interest to continue to attend.

The reluctance of the patient to accept the program probably centers mostly around its unfamiliarity. This suggests the need to explain both the purpose and the rationale of the program in some detail, a procedure that was followed quite thoroughly at some of the programs we visited. At Prairie View Mental Health Center, Dr. Mitchell Jones said, "When we have a person that we think would be served best in the day hospital, we tell him as much as we can about what the program is like, and then his reaction to this information helps us to decide whether the day hospital is in fact the best place for him."

Dr. Wilder said, "I would never describe the day hospital to a person in the emergency room, because no matter what I tell him he will have a fantasy that we're shipping him off somewhere. Assuming that he comes in with his family during the hours that the day hospital is open, I would take him over, then say, 'This would be your nurse. And you notice that everybody wears his own clothes.' Then I would sit down with the patient and the nurse and the relative and have a cup of coffee, and then ask him, 'What do you think? If it doesn't work out, you can always come to the emergency room here.' The majority of patients—probably eighty percent—will say, 'This is great. I wish I had known about it before.' "

Despite the sensibleness of this approach, it appears to represent something of a greater effort than we could discern in some of the facilities we visited. While some had even gone so far as to have pamphlets printed describing the day hospital program, others appeared to feel that the patient should simply be willing to accept that what was being prescribed for him would be the best thing for him. But it appears that many patients assigned to the day hospital do not in fact accept this premise.

A consistent problem among some of the programs was a high early dropout rate (at least in comparison with the dropout rate from inpatient services; the evidence suggests that the dropout rate from outpatient services is phenomenally high). A number of patients after attending for only one or two days or for a week fail to show up again. The response to these "no shows" varied considerably among the facilities. Some telephoned the patient's home within half an hour of the time he was scheduled to arrive. Some paid home visits to truant patients. The Temple University program used its own day patients to make home visits on truant day patients.

Other programs, taking the position that "if the patient is well enough to be on day status, he's well enough to get himself here," took no steps at all to contact patients who do not attend. "The patient may well interpret this attitude as disinterest in his welfare," says Dr. Walter Barton. "Frequently a friendly telephone call to tell the patient that he was missed and to ask whether he will be coming tomorrow will reassure the patient that the staff care about him. We ought to acknowledge with patients, as we do in other relationships, that much of what we do in this life is to please others."

One possible explanation for the high early dropout rate could be, of course, that the patient simply does not find anything in the program that seems useful and worthwhile to him. Many day programs are particularly upsetting to those patients whose expectations are based on their conceptions of medically oriented inpatient services. But we suspect that the major reason is that part-time hospitalization remains an alien concept. Most people do not seem to understand the part-time hospital any more than they understand the part-time jail. Patients are inclined to feel that if they are not sick enough to stay in the hospital at night, then they are not sick enough to need to come to it in the daytime. This brings to mind that the day program appears to be thought of almost universally as a *reduction* of inpatient care rather than as an *extension* of outpatient care. Perhaps what is needed instead of either of these is a new concept of a continuum of care, provided from a single source of supply.

X. The Program

P ERHAPS THE MAJOR characteristic that currently serves to differentiate the high-quality mental health program from other programs is the availability of an active, demanding, and carefully structured program. (This takes for granted an appropriate use of psychotropic medication.) In recent years more and more inpatient facilities have seen the importance of providing such programs, which have come to be commonly called "milieu therapy." The purposes are to provide the patient with psychological and social supports, to encourage him to enhance his oftentimes inadequate social skills, to learn to behave appropriately, and to develop new interests and insights.

If such a program is desirable for the inpatient facility, it is well-nigh mandatory for the day program. Very few patients are willing to take the trouble to commute to a treatment facility simply to sit around. Consequently, if the day program wishes to stay in business, it must offer its patients a variety of activities that have meaning to them.

All of the programs we visited scored high marks in this regard. They were perhaps most similar in the components of their programs. Substantially all of them placed strong emphasis on group methods, procedures, and relationships. All had total community meetings. All engaged at least some of the patients in formally scheduled small group psychotherapy, and some made this a required activity for all patients. By and large, the programs encouraged informal individual transactions between staff members and patients, but only two of the programs engaged all patients in individual psychotherapy, and only two others engaged any considerable number, while one program prohibited it altogether.

The time not devoted to group or individual psychotherapy was for the most part spent in a variety of group, and sometimes individual, activities, including occupational therapy, paid work, numerous kinds of recreational events, and such projects as preparing lunches and dinners.

Many of the programs provided some deliberately unscheduled periods, on the basis that no one can be expected to interact with others more than a certain amount of the time.

Among the programs there were different kinds of approaches. In some there was a clear attempt at democratization, with blurring of the staff-patient roles. In others there was an attempt to impart the message: "This is a hospital, we are professionals, we will assign you to classes and activities, and give you drugs at certain times."

The amount of programmed activity ranged from about three hours per day upward, in most cases for five days a week. Only Mt. Sinai Hospital operated its partial hospitalization services seven days a week, and even then at a somewhat reduced level of activity on weekends.

XI. Staffing the Day Program

O NLY ONE PROGRAM that we visited, the Hawaii Convalescent Center, appeared to be understaffed. All of the others had a ratio of staff to patients that ranged from moderately good to very good. In some cases we felt that there were more professionals than were needed for the relatively small caseloads; there were instances in which there were about as many staff members as there were patients attending. This richness of staffing probably results from two causes: *a*) the fact that many of these day programs were started on an exploratory basis as a somewhat privileged special service, and *b*) a number of them had not built up an average attendance as large as the originally announced capacity.

Almost everywhere we heard the view expressed that the day program is harder on the staff than the inpatient program. This appears to be true, principally for the reason that the patients must be provided an active, daylong program. The other side of the coin, of course, is that for the most part day program staff have their evenings and weekends free.

Keeping in mind the shortage of mental health professionals, we tried throughout our visits to elicit statements of the minimum participation required of psychiatrists, social workers, and other professionals— but without success. The greater the degree to which particular programs considered themselves to follow "the medical model," the less were we able to get a statement of just how much psychiatric time is required. We began to feel that apart from prescribing and supervising medication, there is relatively little that the psychiatrist contributes that stems precisely from his exclusive competence as a psychiatrist. Considering that most of the day programs we visited, and evidently most of those in the country, tend to level out at about ward size, we think that with an average attendance of perhaps twenty and an active caseload of thirty to forty, it may be quite possible to operate such a program with only a half-time psychiatrist. Certainly the most effective therapeutic community that we saw during these visits was at the Temple University Community Mental Health Center day hospital, which, even though headed by a full-time psychiatrist, was the farthest removed from what we understand to be meant by the term "medical model."

Most of the programs were using licensed practical nurses, occupational and recreational therapy assistants, and other more available and less expensive categories of staff with evidently good success. They had been, for the most part, carefully chosen in terms of their personal characteristics, and they had been found quite effective in relating to patients.

Several programs were using "mental health workers," individuals who come from the same social background as the lower-income patients, and who have no special training or preparation for working with mental patients. "Through inservice training," says Dr. Walter Barton, "such persons have become useful in serving as the patient's advocate, interpreting what will be done in the course of treatment and letting him know what is expected of him. They are often adept at communicating how the patient perceives and feels about his treatment. As has often been pointed out, middle-class professionals bring their own middle-class values to situations in which they do not understand the differing cultural background of the patient."

XII. Transportation

G ETTING TO THE day hospital ranged from a slight to a major problem, depending on the size of the area served and the availability
of public transportation. Within the large cities, most of the patients were
reasonably able to travel back and forth, although it sometimes took
well over an hour. Frequently, the patients lacked funds; the welfare
departments sometimes could and sometimes could not provide transportation money.

Only one program, Syracuse Psychiatric Hospital, had provided its
own transportation service, and that only for its special day program
for geriatric patients. Dr. James Prevost expressed the wish that they
had never begun to do so, since it developed that the geriatric patients
would have been able by and large to arrange their own transportation,
and also because this practice led to dissatisfaction among the regular
day patients who had to fend for themselves.

Fort Logan Mental Health Center, serving Denver County and several
adjacent counties, found that the rate of day hospital attendance
depended rather directly upon distance from the hospital. Those parts
of the catchment most distant from the hospital had a proportionately
lower representation among day patients.

Prairie View Mental Health Center at one time had a volunteer who
drove several patients from a town some thirty miles away. This has
been an activity widely proposed for volunteers working in community-
based services, but it raises major questions of insurance and insurability.

We did not glean from our interviews many persuasions about the
maximum distance that it is reasonable to expect patients to be able or
willing to commute. It does seem to us preferable to measure the distance not in miles but in travel time. Dr. D. Ewen Cameron a decade
ago proposed that day hospitals were more feasible for patients who
could travel to them within an hour. This seems as useful a rule of thumb
as any. A careful study of the cost and the therapeutic outcome of a
program that provides transportation in an area where public transportation is poorly developed is badly needed.

XIII. Finances

A NUMBER OF the programs that we visited were under public auspices and provided most of their service without charge. Some of them had fee scales based on income and size of family, but in practice the majority of patients paid very little or nothing. Very few patients had health insurance that provided coverage for partial hospitalization.

In the two private facilities, all patients were charged fees (by the institution, not by the staff), although some of them were paid from welfare, local community mental health service funds, and other third-party sources.

The cost of providing a day of care in the day programs was known only approximately in some of the facilities, since there had been no particular need to cost it out separately. In the Fort Logan Mental Health Center and the Minneapolis Veterans Administration Hospital, where exact figures were available, the cost of day treatment was a little more than half the cost of 24-hour care.

It has been widely assumed that a major impediment to further development of day treatment programs lies in the fact that most health insurance policies will not cover this intensity of treatment. Certainly, it is true that a great many policies do not.* However, the authors know of particular programs located in areas where the prevalent health insurance plans do provide very generous coverage for day treatment, and even so it is a treatment approach used hardly at all in the local psychiatric facilities. Clearly, the exclusion of partial hospitalization by insurance underwriters is both unjustifiable and shortsighted, and the pertinent professional and lay groups in the mental health fields are attempting to eliminate this restriction. But this is only one part of the battle, the other, and perhaps even more important, being the need to educate larger numbers of professionals to the therapeutic advantages of partial hospitalization.

---

*See P. L. Scheidemandel, C. K. Kanno, and R. M. Glasscote: *Health Insurance for Mental Illness.* Joint Information Service, Washington, D. C., 1968.

XIV. A Model for a Day Program

THE FORM a day program will take will depend upon the kind of clientele it seeks to serve and its goals for them, the demographic characteristics of its area of service, and the characteristics of the parent institution.

Assuming that the authors were required to draw up plans for a day program intended to serve acutely ill patients, to be admitted both directly to the day program and on transfer from the inpatient service, we would proceed along these lines:

• If at all possible, the program should take place away from, but near to, the inpatient service. Should it be essential for the program to be housed within a hospital building, it should if possible be located on a separate floor. This would be done to avoid the "medical illness" atmosphere that commonly characterizes inpatient services. But it would be even more preferable to locate the program in a small separate building, perhaps across the street or a block away from the inpatient service. Hopefully the building would appear to be more residential than institutional in character. A large older private home could be well adapted to the requirements of a day hospital.

• If it is not possible to have a separate location, then the next alternative might be to combine the day hospital and the outpatient service. A third alternative would be a combined day hospital-inpatient service. In this latter case it would be critical that day patients outnumber inpatients in order to maintain a stimulating therapeutic atmosphere.

• The day hospital staff should also staff the entry point to the mental health system, where decisions regarding treatment modalities are made. At the very least the intake staff, if not actually working in the day hospital, should have had significant past experience working in day hospitals so that they can make a choice of treatment locus on the basis of personal knowledge.

• The patient load should be held to approximately ward size. The active caseload might be as high as fifty, with a range of attendance from about twenty to forty, and an average of about thirty. It seems desirable to have as many as twenty patients at any given time in order to maintain the group processes that characterize most day treatment

37

programs, while forty is about the largest number with which the staff can hope to have a cohesive group at one time. In programs where the capacity needs to be greater than this, it seems preferable to establish subunits.

• There should be one day a week when the program begins later in the day and continues into the evening, in order to provide a convenient time for family members to attend a therapy session and take part in other programmed activities.

• Some provision would be required for emergencies arising in the evening and on weekends. If the psychiatric program provides service through a general emergency room, the day patients could go there. Otherwise, each day patient should have the telephone number of some member of the staff who would be responsible for responding to emergency calls.

• The staff-patient ratio should probably be in the vicinity of one clinical staff member to each four or five active cases.

• There should be an inclusive rather than an exclusive admission policy.

• The staff hierarchy should be flattened and should be, in general, permissive and less directive than is often the case in traditional services. This should include role definitions that incorporate a delegation of responsibility for tasks to team members, and shared communication, observation, and experience, rather than an authoritarian procedure of the physician giving the nurse an order to carry out.

• The treatment program should be diverse and should permit modification and variation to suit the needs of individual patients.

• Reasonable efforts should be made to arrange acceptable residential placement for patients who do not have families or who should be removed from their families.

• There should be active collaboration with social and vocational rehabilitation agencies.

• Systematic program evaluation should be incorporated, with a plan for long-term follow-up research.

Obviously the cost of providing such a service would vary greatly according to individual circumstances. It would depend, for example, on whether the day unit is responsible for doing its own intakes and patient evaluations, whether it accepts direct admissions of persons with no previous treatment history, and whether it places much emphasis on individual treatment. In the interest, however, of providing at least some tentative idea of the amount of money that might be involved, let us assume a facility with an average daily attendance of thirty, operating five days a week, year-round, with a staff consisting of one psychiatrist, two social workers, two registered nurses, two psychiatric technicians, one occupational therapist, one recreational therapist, one vocational counselor half time, one psychologist two-fifths time, and one secretary. The payroll including benefits would come to approximately $120,000 at prevailing salaries. Allowing $6000 per year for rent or amortization, another $6000 for utilities and maintenance, and $20,000 for drugs and other supplies, the total budget would come to a little more than $150,000. This would break down to approximately $19 per patient per day, for a well-staffed program. This contrasts with a room-and-board charge of something more than $27 for general hospital psychiatric units (the latest figures available are for 1964,* and charges have risen in most general hospitals since that time; furthermore, psychotherapy and medications would be additional). On this basis, one can hypothesize that day treatment might cost, as it does at Fort Logan, about one half as much as inpatient treatment, and perhaps less.

A program intended to serve mainly those persons who require social and vocational rehabilitation, or to maintain substantially impaired persons in the community by means of providing a structured day, would presumably want to place considerably more emphasis on paid work, allowing the patients not only to improve their instrumental and psychosocial vocational skills but in the process to earn some money and to help to cut down the cost of running the facility. The Hawaii Convalescent Center was our sole example of a facility primarily emphasizing service of this nature, and its costs were by far the lowest of any of the programs we visited. While the program operates under a single budget that includes outpatient aftercare service for several hundred patients, the cost of the day treatment aspects can be approximated at $6.50 per patient per day.

Such a program would probably require fewer treatment professionals and, in their place, one or two persons experienced in workshop activities, including obtaining contracts, supervising their fulfillment, and taking care of the financial and administrative aspects.

For either program, the clientele need not be limited solely to persons on day status. Assuming that it is located near the inpatient service, there is no reason why those inpatients able to participate cannot come to the day program. In that such an arrangement would obviate the need for a separately programmed day on the inpatient service, it should serve to lower the cost of staffing the inpatient service.

---

*R. M. Glasscote and C. K. Kanno: *General Hospital Psychiatric Units: A National Survey.* Joint Information Service, Washington, D. C., 1965.

XV. Night and Evening Programs

W E HAVE TENDED throughout the foregoing section to use the terms "day program" and "partial hospitalization" very nearly synonymously. This reflects our conclusion that at this point partial hospitalization is, in fact, very largely limited to day programs. As our report of the statistical survey indicated, we were able to identify only about three dozen night and evening programs. If persons designated for day status are apt to think that being well enough to sleep at home suggests being too well to require day hospitalization, so those designated for evening and night programs seem even more inclined to feel that if they are able to work or go to school during the day, they are well enough to go to their own homes in the evening.

We saw only two evening-night programs in the course of this survey. Both seemed to be successful with their relatively small numbers of patients. Both required, as do all other night and evening programs that we know of, that the patient either be employed, actively looking for work, or in school; in other words, persons idle during the day may not simply elect to be treated in the evening because they prefer it.

The indications for evening and night programs do not yet appear to have been defined. There is some reason to believe that there would be adequate utilization mainly in very large cities that have fair numbers of solitary individuals. The circumstances of persons considered suitable for night and evening hospital appear to be sufficiently different from those of the day patient that this particular intensity of treatment, still in a very rudimentary stage, deserves to be the subject of a separate and full investigation.

XVI. The Weekend Program

THE WEEKEND PROGRAM has as its purpose to provide an intensive therapeutic experience to persons who, with this degree of support, will be able to work or go to school the other five days of the week. There are very few such programs, and there does not yet seem to be a persuasion that it is an intensity of treatment that deserves much emphasis.

It is interesting to note, however, the recent increase in interest in "marathon" group therapy, in which a continuous session may last for 24 hours or more. Since most of these sessions take place on weekends, perhaps they should be viewed as a form of weekend hospitalization.

We were able to find only one weekend program described in the literature. An experimental weekend hospital operated by the Topeka Veterans Administration Hospital* reported good results from a program that emphasized large amounts of group therapy for chronically ill men who came from distances up to one hundred miles.

---

*F. Vernallis and R. Reinert: "The Weekend Hospital," *Mental Hospitals* 14: 254-258, May 1963.

Twelve Program Descriptions

The material that follows should be regarded as descriptions of programs at a particular point in time. Some had changed in some particulars between the time the description was reviewed and approved by the facilities and the time the manuscript was sent to the printer; some will have changed still further during the time that elapsed between sending the manuscript to the printer and the date of publication. They are presented as hopefully useful and instructive examples of partial hospitalization programs at a given stage of their evolution.

Sound View-Throgs Neck Community Mental Health Center

Bronx, New York

THE SOUND VIEW-THROGS NECK Community Mental Health Center is probably the only one in the country to have evolved from a day hospital. The day hospital from which it evolved represents one of the most important research efforts concerning the feasibility of day hospitalization as an alternative to inpatient treatment of the severely mentally ill. The nature and the purpose of the day hospital have changed substantially in the course of the development of the community mental health center program, and further major changes in the day hospital are planned. The history and the present status of this partial hospitalization program and the changes planned for it provide important information bearing upon the entire future of day hospitalization services in the United States.

I. THE EARLY YEARS

What is now the day hospital service of the Sound View-Throgs Neck Community Mental Health Center was established in 1959 as a research program in social and community psychiatry of the Albert Einstein College of Medicine and the Bronx Municipal Hospital Center. Quartered in the East Bronx, in the Westchester Square Health Center building, it was known as the Westchester Square Day Hospital.

The directors of the day hospital research program were Dr. Jack Wilder, now director of the Sound View-Throgs Neck Community Mental Health Center, Dr. Gilbert Levin, now associate director of the same center, and Dr. Israel Zwerling, now director of Bronx State Hospital. Their purpose was to ascertain to what extent persons already evaluated as requiring hospitalization for mental illness could be successfully treated in a day hospital. Their findings* have widely influenced other programs interested in establishing partial hospitalization services.

The study was done in the following way. Of all persons examined by the mental health services of Bronx Municipal Hospital Center and determined to require inpatient care, a stipulated percentage were arbitrarily assigned instead to the day program at Westchester Square. The staff at Westchester Square could refuse to accept particular patients, and they did so in one third of the cases referred to them. Of those "rejected" about one half were persons with chronic brain syndrome. The occasional suicidal or homicidal patient who attended the day hospital was transported from Westchester Square to the inpatient service at Bronx Municipal Hospital Center, where he spent his nights and weekends. All other patients spent their evenings and weekends at home, a procedure that required extensive staff effort with families and with transportation problems.

The day program occupied essentially the same physical space as it does now: an attractive large living room-dining room combination; a modern kitchen where patients make their own lunch; two small occupational therapy rooms; a small beauty shop; a recreation room with a pool table, punching bag, and similar equipment; a small woodworking shop; and a small work-for-pay shop. The treatment program consisted of individual, family, and group therapy. Psychiatric residents saw each patient at least twice a week individually and then together with the family at least once a week. A social worker, sometimes accompanied by the physician, made a visit to the patient's home during evening hours within the first two weeks of his hospitalization.

Despite the considerable extent of individual contact, the underlying therapeutic rationale was group oriented. Each patient was assigned at the time of admission to one of three activity groups, each having from eight to ten patients. Each group was staffed by a psychiatrist, a nurse, and an aide. One-hour morning group discussions were followed by a variety of group activities.

About sixty percent of the patients accepted for day treatment did not require any "boarding" on the inpatient service, and of those who

---

*J. F. Wilder, G. Levin, and I. Zwerling: "A Two-Year Follow-up Evaluation of Acute Psychotic Patients Treated in a Day Hospital," *American Journal of Psychiatry* 122:1095-1101, April 1966. Also, I. Zwerling and J. F. Wilder: "An Evaluation of the Applicability of the Day Hospital in Treatment of Acutely Disturbed Patients," *Israel Annals of Psychiatry and Related Disciplines* 2:162-185, October 1964.

did, the boarding was usually brief and during the first two weeks of hospitalization.

For purposes of evaluating the program, three-part interviews took place. The patient and a family member were seen jointly and asked questions about the patient's and family's behavior since discharge, "including household and living arrangements, outpatient treatment, additional inpatient treatment, family adjustment, work adjustment, social adjustment, and attitudes toward mental illness, and toward the previous hospitalization under study." If the patient had been rehospitalized, information was sought concerning the onset of decompensation, and the point at which the family considered hospitalization necessary and why. Next, the patient and his family member were interviewed separately regarding the patient's adjustment to family, work, children, sex, housekeeping, appearance, and so on. Then the patient and family member were brought together again and asked various attitudinal questions.

All patients assigned to the day hospital with diagnoses other than brain syndrome were considered as day hospital patients whether they were "accepted" or "rejected" by the day hospital. The authors were interested in assessing the effectiveness of the availability of a day hospital to a population of acute nonorganic psychiatric admissions. Treating the day hospital "acceptances" and "rejections" all as day hospital patients prevented any selective biasing of the follow-up data in favor of the day hospital.

It was found that fewer of the day hospital patients were discharged on medication—60 percent for day patients, 80 percent for inpatients. Two years after admission, approximately the same percentage of day hospital patients and inpatients were living in the community (85 percent and 81 percent). Forty percent of the day hospital patients had been rehospitalized at least once, and about forty percent of this group had been rehospitalized more than once. Forty-five percent of the inpatients required rehospitalization. Where readmission occurred, the interval between discharge and first readmission was significantly longer for the day hospital patients.

Any person interested in establishing or encouraging the establishment of a day hospital program should carefully study the reports of this research. It established that with limited selection of patients the substantial majority of patients in most diagnostic categories could be treated in a day program with an outcome generally equivalent to that for persons treated in 24-hour care. This finding ought to have important implications for mental health planning, at a time when it costs $25,000 to $30,000 per bed to build inpatient facilities.

At the same time, it is important to realize that the extremely rich staffing of this research project could not and probably should not be duplicated. There were fourteen professionals for an average census of thirty day patients. It is also necessary to realize that the relative lack of selection of patients called for some heroic efforts to maintain some patients in the community even on weekends and evenings. It would be extremely valuable to see this investigation repeated but with the staffing both of the inpatient and the day service held to a size that might be attainable in the majority of cities in this country.

II. THE DAY HOSPITAL IN 1968

The Westchester Square Day Hospital as a research activity came to a halt when the Sound View-Throgs Neck Community Mental Health Center, an outgrowth of the day hospital, came into being in June 1967. The day hospital is markedly changed. The core nursing and activity staff remain the same, but the professional staff, while retaining some therapeutic responsibility for day hospital patients, spend most of their time on the outpatient service. It no longer seeks to provide an alternative to inpatient care for those who are acutely ill. It has become only one among many components of a comprehensive range of services, and as such has lost some of the prestige that it enjoyed during the time of the research project.

The area served

The community mental health center is responsible for a catchment of 210,000 in the southeastern part of the Bronx. This area has been divided into three subcatchments, called "towns." They are:

1. Throgs Neck, with 40,000 population, predominantly white (Italian and Irish), Catholic, lower-middle class, relatively stable and conservative.

2. Sound View, 100,000 population, until recently almost entirely Jewish, now being rapidly supplanted by a nonwhite population that has reached 25 percent.

3. Tremont, an amalgamation of three contiguous health districts, with a population of 70,000, many of them middle class, the majority living in large housing developments.

The center is divided between two locations. At Jacobi Hospital, one of the two hospitals that make up the Bronx Municipal Hospital Center, there is the previously existing emergency service, staffed by psychiatric residents, and two inpatient wards with a total of 45 beds. At Westchester Square, approximately a mile away, are located the outpatient teams, the day hospital, and the activity center. Although an affiliated rather than an integral part of the mental health center, Bronx State Hospital operates four "Sound View-Throgs Neck wards" of forty patients each. In the community there are transitional residences for sixty persons and a prevocational workshop for fifty persons.

Capacity and range of census

The stated capacity of the day hospital had not changed much since the days of the research program. There were openings for 30 patients. During 1967 the census ranged from 18 to 27. In mid-January 1968, 21 patients attended in the course of a week, almost all of them coming for five days.

The staff

The day program is headed by a young British psychiatrist, Dr. James Todd, who served as an assistant to Dr. Maxwell Jones at Dingleton Hospital in Scotland. He had been on the staff only three months at the time of our visit. His role was essentially one of supporting the nurses, who run the day-to-day program. Dr. Todd was not directly involved with patients except at a weekly meeting of all patients and all staff.

Three registered nurses head up the day hospital's three subunits, which correspond to the three "towns" that make up the catchment. These jurisdictional lines are not strictly observed, however; in the event that one subunit has patients almost entirely of one or two diagnoses, some adjustment can be made by the assignment of new patients. Each nurse is assisted by an aide.

The nurses and aides meet with Dr. Todd for an hour each morning. Then each nurse meets with her patients for a one-hour group therapy session, followed by two hours of group activity. There are three recreational therapists and an occupational therapist who serve the entire program, providing a large variety of specialized activities.

The three nurses were extremely impressive. With relatively little assistance, they seemed to carry the bulk of the treatment. Their level of sophistication and the quality of their work seemed to be extremely high. Our visit was made the morning following the assassination of Dr. Martin Luther King; the nurses on their own initiative had canceled the customary morning program in order to conduct a community meeting to deal with the feelings about the assassination among the racially mixed group of patients.

Referrals

The day hospital is not an entry point, and it receives referrals from one source only, namely the "town teams." These multidisciplinary teams and the manner of their operation are among the most interesting aspects of this program. A team staff member functions much as a family physician, caring for the patient in all phases of illness, with the exception of inpatient care. Each town has a psychiatrist and a social worker assigned to the inpatient service. The town professionals—psychiatrists, psychologists, social workers, community organizers, and mental health rehabilitation workers—provide all outpatient treatment and much of the consultation and education service conducted in the community. While all of them are physically housed in the Westchester Square building, certain of them spend varying amounts of time deployed in satellite clinics and other facilities in their respective neighborhoods. In time, with the development of more multiservice centers in the Bronx, the teams will spend proportionately more of their time "in the field."

The professionals, principally the psychiatrists, see patients very much along a private practice model. Specifically, rather than holding "clinic hours," they work by appointment. If it is determined by the emergency service at Jacobi Hospital that a patient brought there does not require inpatient care, the Jacobi staff will telephone Westchester Square to make a definite appointment for him to be seen there.

When a Jacobi inpatient has shown enough improvement that release from inpatient treatment can soon be anticipated, that patient will be transferred to the jurisdiction of the town team serving the area where he lives. He will probably have met his town psychiatrist in the course of one of the liaison visits which the town teams make each week to the town representatives on the inpatient service.

If the town psychiatrist determines that a particular patient will need more contact and support than can be provided through outpatient appointments alone, he can arrange for the patient to come to the Westchester Square program either as a day patient or to engage, in the afternoon only, in the activity program there. The town psychiatrist and his team will continue to see the patient even while he participates in the day hospital program. The contact may be as often as two appointments per week or as infrequent as a monthly medication check. There is an informal "liaison" between the day hospital nurse and the town team, sometimes scheduled, sometimes sporadic; in addition each nurse attempts to keep the town teams regularly advised of pertinent developments with particular patients.

Characteristics of the patients

We have indicated that the day hospital is now rarely used for patients in the most acute phase of illness. From the time the center started, 65 percent of day hospital patients have been persons referred by the town teams, immediately following an episode of hospitalization at Jacobi. The remaining 35 percent are admitted directly from the community.

During 1967 a total of 118 persons were on day status, about two fifths of them men. Seventy-eight percent were between 21 and 65 years old, 17 percent were under 21, and five percent were over 65. By far the largest diagnostic group was schizophrenic reactions (50 percent), followed by psychoneuroses (22 percent), psychotic depressions (11 percent), and personality disorders (six percent).

By social and economic status, the patients appear to correspond generally with the characteristics of the catchment, although there was some indication that Negroes and Puerto Ricans were underrepresented. The limited number of Puerto Ricans may be related to language problems. While in the past there have been Spanish-speaking persons on the staff, there were none at the time of our visit. We were told that persons who do not speak English are more likely to be seen in the outpatient service, where interpreters are available.

Treatment philosophy

This community mental health center sees as its first priority service to persons disabled by either acute or chronic mental illness. Preventive activities are indicated as the second priority, and efforts to "promote optimal living for all" are the third priority. At this early stage, the center is already seeing persons at the rate of more than two thousand per year. "It is impossible to make long-term intensive one-to-one commitments to so many patients," said Dr. Wilder. There is great emphasis on the need for continuity of care, and it is principally on this point that the operation of the day hospital will be changed (as described below). The program is noteworthy for the spectrum of services it renders, with major emphasis on the need to furnish maintenance and support over a very long period of time.

Within the day hospital, the emphasis has particularly changed. In the days of the research program there was much attention to group process, particularly in respect of improving the social skills of the patients. At the time of our visit there seemed to be less emphasis on attempting to bring about change in the patient and more emphasis on maintaining him, but this is probably related to the already described change in the characteristics of the clientele served.

The treatment program

Much of the treatment program has been incorporated in the description above of the staff. We should mention that home visits, made routinely during the research phase, are now made only occasionally, and by the town therapists.

Another important change has been to limit the formal day hospital program to the hours from 9 a.m. to 1 p.m. Following the morning group sessions and activities, the day patients spend about an hour and a half preparing and serving lunch. The afternoon from 1 p.m. to 4 p.m. is devoted to a differently structured activities program, in which the day patients are joined by any number of persons who are in outpatient treatment, or were former inpatients or day patients. More than twenty small group activities are held during the week including ceramics, art, grooming, community activities, and current events. On a given day the total number, including the day hospital patients, ranges from about 25 to 75 persons. Day hospital patients rejoin the day hospital staff for an informal meeting just prior to going home.

Day hospital patients are advised that in case of an upset at night or on the weekend they are to report to the emergency service at Jacobi Hospital. The names of day hospital patients and the telephone numbers of the therapists are kept on file there. The resident on duty decides whether or not the patient would benefit from a transfer to the inpatient service. If he is hospitalized overnight, the resident notifies the Westchester Square psychiatrist the following morning and the two of them determine whether the patient should remain for the time being on the inpatient service or whether he should resume at once in the day hospital.

A major activity that we felt can certainly be considered an important part of therapy is the canteen run by the day patients. With a minimum of supervision they prepare delicious lunches that are bought by the staff and patients. The proceeds are used to finance various group activities.

Transportation

We have mentioned that the program is located near a transportation center and is therefore reasonably available by public transportation. Dr. Wilder believes that efforts to ascertain the reasons for underutilization of day hospital programs in urban areas have overemphasized transportation problems.

Placements

This program does more than most to help patients find jobs and places to live. Two adjacent houses with four apartments and common recreation rooms and gardens, accommodating twenty persons, are owned by a private foundation and serve the mental health center exclusively. Each house has a houseparent. Four to six tenants of the same sex share each apartment. Tenants who spend their days working or studying pay a lower rent than those who are unoccupied. Residents may stay as long as a year and can participate in all nonhospital programs.

The center also operates individual apartments in the community, where twenty graduates of the halfway house may live without a time limit. It has also arranged foster home placements for about twenty patients.

The center operates a sheltered workshop at Bronx State Hospital, involving at the time of our visit 53 patients. Since the capacity at any one time is 18 patients, they work in shifts of a few hours a week each. They are paid at the rate of 90 cents per hour. Day hospital patients are eligible for placement there, but in practice they constitute only a few of the group; at the time of our visit there were three day patients in the program. A huge workshop capable of serving two hundred workers is under construction. It is supported by the same foundation that owns the halfway house.

Financing

The funds for this community mental health center are derived principally from the City of New York and from the federal government staffing grant. Fees are levied according to a sliding scale, with a maximum charge of $37.50 per day for persons attending the day hospital. In practice the majority pay nothing, about a third pay some small portion, and only about two percent pay the full amount.

The evening program

The same staff that run the day program are also responsible for an evening activities program, operating from 7 to 9 p.m. on Monday through Thursday evenings, and every fourth Friday evening. Its stated capacity is fifty per evening. During a week in mid-January 1968, a total of fifty different persons attended. A broad variety of group activities is offered.

Future plans

We have mentioned that a major change was planned for this day hospital, primarily to ensure continuity of care. In this situation lie some of the basic problems of operating partial hospitalization services.

The day hospital has found it difficult to coordinate its efforts with those of the inpatient and the outpatient services. The difficulty with the inpatient service is believed to arise from the fact that it is operated by staff who on the one hand have had no personal exposure to partial hospitalization as a treatment arrangement and on the other hand are reluctant to give up their patients at an early stage when they are just beginning to form a relationship.

The difficulty with the outpatient service seems to arise from the arrangement whereby "outside" therapists have treatment responsibility for the day patients. In interviewing three of the town psychiatrists, we noted a reluctance to refer to the day hospital. These three intelligent and enthusiastic young psychiatrists had had relatively little experience with day hospitalization during their training, and none at all with a separately operated day hospital program. They insisted that many of their outpatients were indeed the same kinds of persons who are placed in 24-hour care elsewhere, and since they felt that these patients were being adequately maintained as outpatients (although in many cases with the added involvement in the afternoon and evening activity groups) they could see little reason to refer them to the day hospital.

Dr. Wilder had concluded arrangements to incorporate the day hospital into the Jacobi Hospital program, so that it may once more serve acutely ill patients. He envisioned a plan whereunder the day patients and inpatients would come together each morning for a unified program, then in the afternoon would split up for separate programs. He believes that in this way it will be possible to engage a larger proportion of patients in day treatment, since the reluctance of the inpatient physician to refer the patient elsewhere will presumably be overcome in a partially unified inpatient-day hospital arrangement where the same staff will provide treatment both to inpatients and to day patients.

The Westchester Square day program will then become a full-fledged and full-time activity program. A number of the kinds of patients now served there in the day hospital program can continue to attend, one assumes with approximately the same effect as at present. In addition there will be a much broader and larger program of activities available to help maintain a larger number of patients and former patients who need more contact than simply outpatient appointments. The change from "hospital status" to "clinic status" will also open up the facility for more activity groups for children.

When the large sheltered workshop mentioned above becomes available it will serve the patients who cannot make the grade in existing vocational rehabilitation programs. "Any person who needs work and cannot get it by reason of the deficit caused by his illness will be able to work in our sheltered workshop for as long as necessary," Dr. Wilder said.

Some observations

The Westchester Square Day Hospital answered some important questions about partial hospitalization. Its successor, the Sound View-Throgs Neck Community Mental Health Center, raises some new questions.

If, as the town psychiatrists in this program maintain, most disturbances except those involving homicidal or suicidal behavior can be handled on an outpatient basis, plus part-time activity programs, is there a real need for formal day hospital programs? Or as one of the consultants put it, "To wax cynical, since there is almost no scientific evidence regarding the relative effectiveness of inpatient, day hospital, and outpatient care, why not place patients in the cheapest treatment modality, as long as the community will tolerate it?"

It will be of particular interest to see how this well-staffed, enthusiastic, and comprehensive service will fare in respect of its new procedure for delivering day hospital care. If it is found under the new arrangement that substantial numbers of seriously ill persons can be handled on day clinic status, the program will have provided additional evidence of the need for such programs, assuming that the various obstacles to partial hospitalization can be worked out without having to go to preposterous lengths. Yet the decline, even for the time being, in the use of day hospitalization in this program raises the question of whether the day hospital is worth all the trouble. The question is still open.

State Convalescent Center
Honolulu

THE STATE CONVALESCENT CENTER, an agency of the Division of Mental Health of the Hawaii Department of Health, includes an outpatient clinic, a day hospital unit, and a quasi-independent workshop. With a very small staff and budget, it provides a great volume of service to a very sick population.

Established in 1958, the Convalescent Center is one of two major components of the state mental health program in Hawaii. The second is Hawaii State Hospital, located about twenty miles from Honolulu, and serving all of the several islands that make up the state of Hawaii. The census of the state hospital at its peak, in the mid-1950's, was 1350 patients. Today it is around 650, while the Convalescent Center carries a caseload of equal size. The staff of the Convalescent Center were quick to point out that they could not know to what extent it was the advent of psychotropic drugs and to what extent it was the establishment of the Convalescent Center that accounted for this substantial drop in state hospital census. However, one may observe that between 1956 and 1966 the drop in state hospital census on a nationwide basis was 26 percent, whereas in Hawaii it was about 50 percent.

Physical plant

The Convalescent Center is located in a residential section of Honolulu, near Diamond Head and close to the city limits.

It was of particular interest to us that the staff felt a different type of physical setting was desirable, mainly on the grounds that the present one was too institutional. To our view, it was the least institutional of all that we saw in our visits. Although the large rectangular building is somewhat Spartan, it is made of attractive stained wood and is surrounded by a screened lanai, most of its external walls are open to the breeze, and from many rooms there are views of lush greenery. But we were told that the lanai is too small for activities, that the center is too close to the neighboring tuberculosis hospital, that the central corridor is too dark. This building was formerly a unit of a tuberculosis hospital; the previous home of the Convalescent Center was a former school, where instead of a long central corridor there was an open central courtyard with a fountain, which provided a natural center for informal social gatherings.

The present two-story facility is commodious, with offices, dayrooms, and several large workshops.

Capacity and range of census

The stated capacity of the day hospital is 75 persons, but the attendance frequently exceeds that number. During 1967 the range of daily attendance was 42 to 110. During a week in January 1968 there were 49 patients who attended five days, 27 more who attended three days, 50 more who attended two days, and 42 more who attended one day.

The staff

The same staff serve both the outpatient and the day hospital functions, although with some specialization; specifically, the nurses devote proportionately more of their time to the day hospital, while the social workers devote proportionately more to the outpatient clinic. The two psychiatrists—a full-time director, Dr. Bienvenido Garcia, and a four-fifths time staff psychiatrist—spend the great majority of their time supervising the medication checkup of patients, and since there are about three times as many outpatients as day patients they consequently devote most of their time to the outpatients.

The total staff for the combined outpatient-day hospital activities include, in addition to the two psychiatrists, a psychologist, four social workers, two registered nurses, three aides, and an occupational therapist. Each of these staff members was carrying a patient load that would be considered overwhelming even in most purely custodial settings. A survey of staff activities covering eleven working days in early 1968 showed that the two psychiatrists spent 94 hours in direct patient contact, seeing 235 patients for an average of 24 minutes each. During this same period the social workers had 55 contacts and the nurses 123 contacts with outpatients alone. We interviewed all except one or two members of the staff, and each one, when asked what he felt the program's greatest need to be, said, More staff. Clearly these people were working under extremely demanding circumstances. It was therefore interesting to note that their morale was extremely high, and the evidence of the outcome of their efforts indicates that they are remarkably successful.

Both because the staff is small in size and because the feeling among staff members seems to be very good, all of them are readily accessible to one another. Most of their patient contacts are *ad hoc,* based on the needs of particular patients; there are two intake conferences and one staff conference per week.

In terms of ratio, for each staff member there are about fourteen day patients and about forty outpatients. We know of day hospital programs where there are more staff members than patients, and where the evidence of the outcome of treatment is less favorable than in this program. If one accepts that there is a shortage of mental health professionals, the implications of this program are of great importance. One must note, however, that there has been a heavy turnover of psychiatric personnel. The program has had six directors during its ten years. A principal reason for this turnover appears to be the strain of the exceptionally heavy work load.

The psychiatrist-director had been with the program since early 1966 and was planning to leave, both because of the inordinate demands of the job and the relatively low salary. He has ultimate responsibility both for the day program and the outpatient service. The supervisor of the day program from its inception has been a registered nurse, Mrs. Mary Simon. She is a major motive force; she provides continuity and charisma.

At the time of our visit volunteer time came to about 24 hours per week. The principal activities of volunteers with patients are to take them on outings and to lead groups in art, dancing, community singing, and so on. Volunteers also work in the office, compiling statistics and keeping records up to date.

Referrals

The great majority of patients seen at the Convalescent Center—92 percent—come there on referral from the state hospital. This figure includes a few that are first referred by the state hospital to one of the outpatient clinics run by the state and thence to the Convalescent Center. Another four percent are referred by the psychiatry service at Queen's Hospital, a general hospital in Honolulu where the state will pay for psychiatric care for a period not exceeding thirty days, for those who cannot afford private care. The remaining four percent come equally on referral from private physicians and from social agencies. In 1967 the figures were as follows:

From Hawaii State Hospital	256
From Queen's Hospital	10
From private physicians	6
From social agencies	6

Selection procedure

We were told that the following categories of patients are not admitted: *a*) those with acute brain syndrome; *b*) those who are acutely disturbed and violent; *c*) persons below the age of twelve; *d*) alcoholics; *e*) drug addicts; *f*) persons so depressed as to present a suicide risk.

Characteristics of the patients

This program was among the best that we visited in terms of its knowledge of the characteristics of the patients it serves.

The substantial majority of patients—74 percent in 1967—are diagnosed as schizophrenic. Psychotic depressions account for an additional nine percent, and no other diagnosis accounts for more than three percent.

There are slightly more men than women—53 percent vs. 47 percent; this is consistent with the population of Hawaii State Hospital. The average age of the men attending the day hospital is 40 years, with a range from 14 to 69. The average age for women is 44 years, with a range from 19 to 72. A substantial majority of the men—80 percent—have never been married, while 64 percent of the women either are or have been married. The program's psychologist, Dr. Donald DeKrey, commented, "It is unclear whether the large proportion of single patients is related to the type of program offered by the day hospital, or whether it is more directly related to the mental illness, particularly in the case of schizophrenic patients."

A number of the single people live with their primary families, but a larger number live apart from relatives, in rooming or boarding houses.

Dr. DeKrey had also analyzed the patients in terms of national origin. The Japanese population far outnumbers other ethnic groups and is out of proportion to that of the general population of Hawaii; specifically, about 34 percent of the residents of Hawaii are of Japanese background, whereas among the day hospital patients the Japanese account for 48 percent. The reasons for this were not known.

Because the staff were interested in knowing whether the day hospital was no more than "a baby-sitting operation for the chronic, regressed mental patient," the degree of patient movement since the day hospital was established was measured according to the year of original contact for all the persons attending the program during September 1967. It was found that of the 165 persons who attended during that month 60 percent had made their initial contact within the previous three years, and almost half of these within the previous nine months. The remaining 40 percent, in terms of initial contact, were rather evenly distributed over the first seven years of the program's operation. Of the longer-term patients, 93 percent were schizophrenic and/or brain damaged.

"Because attendance is primarily voluntary, with little pressure exerted on the patients, we decided that one measure of the patient's acceptance of the program would be the percent of attendance," Dr. DeKrey said. He found that during September 1967 about a quarter of the patients attended the total amount of time designated for them, and exactly half attended eighty percent or more of the designated time.

The great majority of the patients have been previously hospitalized for mental illness, many of them on more than one occasion. The average number of previous hospitalizations was 3.25 for the men and 3.45 for the women.

Mrs. Simon characterized the patients as falling into these groups:

• A large proportion are patients who have been discharged from Hawaii State Hospital as having received maximum hospital benefit. They require supportive care, including medication, over a long period of time, and most of them will continue to function at a minimal level.

• Another sizable group are those who have been discharged from the hospital following their first admission and who have a fairly good prognosis for rehabilitation.

• A somewhat smaller group are those who were discharged in good condition and went directly to a job, then deteriorated and were referred to the day hospital in preference to being returned to the state hospital.

• The smallest group are those who have never been in the state hospital, and who are sent to the day hospital by privately practicing psychiatrists and general practitioners as an alternative to full-time hospital care.

The staff view the program as providing the support that makes the difference between community living and hospitalization. Said Dr. DeKrey, "Practically all of our patients are ex-hospital patients who are either on their way out or on their way in. Without the support that they get here, well over half of them would soon have to go back. For many of them it's a circular activity; they go to the state hospital, they're released to us, eventually we get them on outpatient status, then they have a relapse, come back to the day hospital or go to the state hospital. But we sustain many of them for a considerable period of time. We feel it's far better for them to be sustained here than in the state hospital."

The treatment program

The day hospital relies principally on medication and work for its therapeutic program. Substantially all of the patients are on psychotropic drugs, and the majority of them participate at some level in the work-for-pay program. There are individual appointments for medication follow-up, and each patient is seen as well by the nurses, the social service staff, and others, as indicated. These appointments are usually brief, often at the patient's request, and generally concerned with day-to-day problems.

The program emphasizes the importance of enabling as many patients as possible to get into competitive, self-supporting work.

The occupational therapy activities are focused almost entirely on evaluating each patient's work potential. Those who are unable to compete in the regular labor market but who have the capability to meet the production demands of a sheltered workshop are placed in the program of Lanakila Crafts, an extensive nonprofit program that is located near downtown Honolulu. Also, a few patients are placed by the Division of Vocational Rehabilitation counselors at Goodwill Industries, another sheltered workshop, and at the Salvation Army, which has its own rehabilitation program. Those whose capability is even more limited can work in the Lanakila Crafts Annex, located in the Convalescent Center. There, under contracts from local businesses, they make small items such as dustpans, deodorant soap bars, wood cabinets, tables, and chairs.

To a large extent the patients are divided into a "faster" and a "slower" group, in terms of their anticipated potential for rehabilitation. The faster group comes on Monday, Wednesday, and Thursday, the slower group on Tuesday and Friday. However, any patient may come on additional days if he wishes, or if it is therapeutically indicated, and the modal attendance is in fact five days a week.

A minority of the patients are involved in a variety of activities, including art class, woodcrafts, sewing, community singing, ceramics, and cooking. There are also community service projects, field trips, outdoor sports, and table games. There is a weekly psychodrama session involving a few patients, and in the months preceding our visit several group therapy units had been established, involving altogether about forty patients.

It will be seen that the primary emphasis in this program is therefore on activities as a means of fostering personal and social interaction with particular attention to vocational rehabilitation, rather than on psychotherapy or on a therapeutic community. The group exists to provide a sense of membership and of support and not to be used as a deliberate therapeutic tool in and of itself.

The average stay for patients discharged during 1967 was seven and one-half months.

Disposition. Out of 246 persons who were on day hospital status during 1967, only 24, or ten percent, were transferred to the state hospital. This is approximately the same as the nationwide transfer rate to state hospitals from general hospital psychiatric units; for the type of patient being dealt with in this program it is extremely low. An additional 69 patients were transferred to outpatient status within the Convalescent Center. Many of these were persons who had been rehabilitated to the point of accepting full-time employment.

Outcome. This program, more than most, is able to gauge its outcome precisely on the basis of disposition of patients. Since substantially all of its patients come from the state hospital, the very fact that it is able to sustain the great majority of them in a community program is in itself an important indication of success. That an additional 69, or 28 percent of all those on day hospital status in 1967, were transferred to a lesser intensity of care (i.e., outpatient status) is an important further indication of successful outcome. It was very striking that this sparsely staffed agency had more complete data on its patient characteristics, utilization of staff time, and program effectiveness than did other day hospitals with ten times its staff-patient ratio.

Records

An examination of a small number of records corroborated all that we had been told about the characteristics of these patients. Most of them had a long history of profound mental illness. The records were of good quality. They reflected some need for additional medical time to allow a more penetrating pursuit of some of the patients' complaints of physical illness.

Transportation

The Convalescent Center is reasonably accessible by public transportation, although for those who live on the far side of the city or on other parts of the island, a rather long ride is involved. A study of where the patients live showed that distance does not seem to be an impediment up to seven miles whereafter there is a sharp drop-off. The patient population includes only a few persons who live outside the city limits of Honolulu. Patients who are welfare clients are eligible to receive funds for bus fare, and in occasional instances the welfare department will pay taxi fare for patients.

Agency relationships

The already described collaboration with Lanakila Crafts is one of the most important agency relationships of this program. Participants in the Lanakila program are referred to the Division of Vocational Rehabilitation, which acts as the coordinating agency for the patient's total vocational program. DVR also furnishes such additional services as testing and counseling, special training, direct job placement, and referral to state and federal retraining programs.

There is also close cooperation with the state hospital; indeed, if there were not it is unlikely that the Convalescent Center could operate satisfactorily.

Residential placements

There are available state-approved boardinghouses, rooming houses, and apartments. The social workers are very active in finding suitable placements for patients who have no families or who have unsuitable families.

Financing

The budget for this program is remarkably small—well under $250,000 per year. This includes approximately $20,000 for drugs that are furnished to most of the patients without charge; however, those who can afford it are asked to pay, no matter how small the amount. While the outpatient and day hospital expenses are combined in a single budget, one can approximate the cost of a day of care in the day hospital at about $6.50—a small fraction of the cost in some of the day programs that we know of.

It is felt important for the patients to pay something, even if only 25 cents per month. Even so, slightly more than half of the patients pay nothing at all. The maximum that any patient pays is $7.50 per month.

Future plans

The Hawaii program of mental health services is presently undergoing reorganization, as part of which the Convalescent Center was discontinued as an entity in mid-1968. The day hospital program of the center has been split, one portion remaining at the center's physical plant but as a component of the Diamond Head Mental Health Center, and the other portion going to the Lanakila Mental Health Center on the far side of Honolulu. Mrs. Simon and other Convalescent Center personnel form the staff of the day hospital of the Diamond Head Center. Dr. Garcia, who became chief of the Lanakila Center in July 1968, and the rest of the center's day hospital staff have started a day hospital program at Lanakila. While most of the Convalescent Center's patients have been assigned to the Diamond Head Center, a substantial number, almost two hundred, have been assigned to the Lanakila Center. Thus, as a result of the reorganization, there are now two day hospitals in the state's mental health program, both staffed with people highly skilled and experienced in day hospital operation.

Fort Logan Mental Health Center*
Denver

A STATE FACILITY serving metropolitan Denver and surrounding counties, Fort Logan Mental Health Center was established in 1961 with the avowed intention of treating as many patients as possible in a day program rather than in a 24-hour program. At all times its day census has been substantially higher than its inpatient census, from time to time more than twice as high. This facility has probably the largest and certainly one of the most important day hospital programs in the world.

Fort Logan, with special programs for alcoholics, geriatric patients, and children, with a crisis intervention service, with halfway houses, and numerous other elements, is a particularly comprehensive facility. The description that follows has been deliberately limited to the adult psychiatry service.

Physical plant

Fort Logan Mental Health Center is located in southwest Denver, just within the city limits, about eleven miles from downtown, on a three-hundred-acre site that formerly was an army post. A number of the old army buildings are still standing, and several of them are used by the mental health center. New construction began in 1961 and continued over the next several years, as additional services were added. There are at present thirteen principal new buildings, three of which are "cottages" that provide sleeping accommodations for inpatients and day-rooms and offices for the treatment program that combines both inpatients and day patients. Each cottage houses two treatment teams and their patients; two are used by the adult psychiatry service, the other by the alcoholism treatment program. There is a large administration building adjacent to a five-story research and education building, the wings of which house the gymnasium, an auditorium, and additional

---

*The description of Fort Logan Mental Health Center was prepared by Mr. Glasscote and Dr. Jepson.

65

treatment areas. Across the street from the administration building is a building with a medical wing and two geriatric units with 25 beds each, and one block away is a children's unit with facilities for 60 inpatients.

All of the new buildings are extremely pleasant and inviting. There is extensive use of glass and of light cheerful colors. Several of the buildings are connected by sheltered walkways. Some buildings have inner courts that are used in the recreation program. The first buildings to be completed had various security features, such as special screens, windows, and doors in some of the patient rooms, but these features have been eliminated from the more recent buildings. The complex of new construction gives the impression of tasteful contemporary design.

The original buildings of the old army post are also appealing, with their high ceilings and large rooms and generous exterior proportions. However, they are difficult to heat, clean, and maintain. One of the original buildings houses the very large work therapy program, two others are used as halfway houses, and another houses the homemaking arts program. Some of the other old buildings are used as temporary housing for new staff members while they locate private housing.

When asked what features of the physical plant she would change if the designs were now being drawn, the director, Dr. Ethel Bonn, said that she would design the cottages so that each would house only one treatment team and its patients, with a greater amount of space for offices and meeting rooms. Also she would enlarge the dayrooms in each cottage, and air-condition and carpet all of the patient areas.

Capacity and range of census

The children's program, the geriatric program, and the alcoholism program all have only a small number of persons on day status, principally as the result of transportation problems peculiar to these special groups. The description that follows and the statistics incorporated in it refer to the psychiatric program for adults.*

The various adult psychiatry teams have available a total bed capacity of only 146 while in the same combined program they can also serve as many as 300 day patients. During fiscal 1967 (July 1966-June 1967) the range of the daily census of day patients was from 170 to 262. The census for a date late in March 1968 showed 109 inpatients, or 75

*The data that follow were supplied by the Fort Logan Record System Project, which is supported in part by Public Health Service Grant No. 5-R11-MH-00931-05 from the National Institute of Mental Health.

percent of bed capacity, and 183 day patients; on that particular date there were thus 68 percent more day patients than inpatients. These figures do not by any means, however, indicate the complete extent of the treatment load of Fort Logan, and the reader may find it interesting to see the breakdown for that same day of all patients under the auspices of the adult psychiatry program.

24-hour patients	109
Day patients	183
Outpatients	404
Family care (foster homes)	81
Home care*	33
Evening patients	19
Halfway house (at Fort Logan)	18
The Lodge (sheltered living and working group in downtown Denver)	10
Special leave	4

With only 146 beds, the adult psychiatry service was carrying an active treatment load of 861.

The staff

Because the program for inpatients and day patients is combined, there are no staff members assigned particularly to day treatment. Altogether there are approximately five hundred full-time and about twenty part-time clinical employees, for all programs combined. Approximately two hundred of the full-time employees are assigned primarily or exclusively to the adult psychiatry service. The majority of these persons make up the ten treatment teams, nine of which are assigned on a geographic basis, with six of these nine serving segments of Denver County and the other three serving the outlying counties. The tenth team is assigned to a special program for long-term patients.

A typical treatment team consists of one psychiatrist, one psychologist, two social workers, seven nurses, seven psychiatric technicians (aides), an activities therapist, and a vocational counselor. Each team serves a total patient group ranging from about 80 to 120 persons. Because of the limited number of beds no more than 14 of this group can be inpatients, and typically there will be about twice as many day patients as inpatients and about twice as many outpatients as day patients.

---

*A special program providing psychiatric treatment, usually family therapy, in the patient's home, funded under the NIMH Hospital Improvement Project.

There was more emphasis in this program on expansion of professional roles than in any other that we visited; related to this was a considerable amount of experimentation in using persons other than psychiatrists to head up the teams. Said Dr. Bonn, "Role expansion has been carefully defined to mean the acquisition and implementation of additional roles by any discipline, beyond those usually assigned to persons having certain formal qualifications. Role expansion is conditional on the individual's interests, aptitudes, and skills, as well as on legal requirements." At the time of our visit, in April 1968, all of the permanent team leaders in adult psychiatry were psychiatrists; shortly afterward the appointments of four nonpsychiatrist team leaders were also made permanent. There appears to be great emphasis on personal characteristics and contributions of individual staff members, as contrasted with formal credentials.

It is important to mention the evidently high quality of the psychiatric nurses and technicians, who appear to be among the most praiseworthy products of Fort Logan's inventiveness. With about 130 nurses and 150 technicians, they comprise together a little over half of all the clinical personnel. These are usually young persons, many of them recent graduates. Technicians, who must be high school graduates, are given six months' training within the program, including about four hundred hours in formal classes. The nurses are given extensive inservice training soon after employment and regularly thereafter. They appear to be highly motivated and to relate successfully both to patients and to fellow staff members.

Unlike many programs, Fort Logan uses registered nurses mainly for working directly with patients and staff, particularly the technicians, with a minimum of administrative tasks. The technicians have been somewhat hampered by the lack of a body of integrated knowledge, and by being subprofessionals. There has been a high turnover rate among technicians because their salary is permanently tied by the civil service system to the level of a high school graduate. An academic mental health worker program leading to an associate of arts degree has been started at a nearby college. As more and more technicians graduate from this program, technician positions at the center will be replaced by mental health worker positions.

The multidisciplinary team has been successfully developed at Fort Logan through the application of intersupporting administrative, supervisory, and educational principles. Team staff are accountable for their work performance to their team leader, who works cooperatively with the chiefs of the clinical disciplines in supporting and maintaining the professional standards of each. Promotions are based on the recommendations of the team leader, with the concurrence of the division chief and the discipline chiefs.

There are inservice training programs in group process and group therapy, community mental health, sensitivity training, and supervision and management. A nursing instructor is assigned part time to each team for on-the-spot consultation and teaching for the entire team. Consultants from within and outside Fort Logan visit the teams and provide additional learning opportunities. The chiefs of the clinical disciplines, the nursing instructors, the specialty chiefs in group therapy and psychodrama, and the consultants are grouped together administratively as the Staff Development department, headed by a psychiatrist responsible to the director. "This degree of continuous training and teaching is essential to a decentralized operation," said Dr. Bonn. "In many ways, each team must function as if it were a small mental health center."

There is an extensive and highly successful volunteer program. At the time of our visit a total of 84 persons and ten organizations were contributing an aggregate of 325 volunteer hours per week, in recreation, in occupational and work therapy, in physical therapy, in the home arts program, in the community clinics, and on assignments both to daytime and evening treatment programs. Some work as staff aides in the admissions office, nursing education, the dietary department, social service, and the Staff Development office. Others help the ward clerks of the treatment teams. During the summer months, 80 to 100 high school and college students serve as volunteers in approximately 25 different departments. They have been found particularly valuable in working on a one-to-one basis with children. A number of these students are considering the mental health field as a career. Said Dr. Bonn, "The volunteers not only help us with the work load, they also benefit the patients, who need contact with community people who are not psychiatrically oriented. They also serve a valuable purpose in interpreting Fort Logan's mission and accomplishments to the community."

The volunteer auxiliary, whose membership includes not only those who do volunteer work at Fort Logan but other persons from the community as well, has sponsored various fund-raising functions. They operate the gift shop, and they run educational programs for the volunteers.

There are also about 35 garden clubs and 200 other community organizations that have helped to raise funds, have donated equipment, furnished entertainment, and taught classes to patients on gardening, bridge, personal grooming, flower arranging, and crafts.

Referrals and selection procedure

A total of 1543 persons were on partial hospitalization status during fiscal 1967. Of these, 965, or 63 percent, were Fort Logan patients who were transferred from inpatient to partial hospitalization status. The remaining 578, or 37 percent, came from a number of different sources, as follows:

	Number	*Percent of admissions directly to day status*
Self-referred	133	*23*
Private psychiatrists	107	*19*
Relatives, friends	81	*14*
Denver General Hospital	58	*10*
Private physicians	47	*8*
Colorado General Hospital	45	*8*
Mental health clinics	20	*3*
Social agencies	18	*3*
Courts, parole officers, police	12	*2*
Clergy	11	*2*
Others, unknown	46	*8*

A remarkable aspect of Fort Logan is the fact that this state facility is allowed to exclude any admission it sees fit, except for patients admitted under court order and commitment. Probably this is true of no other state hospital in the country, except for small training and research institutions. The reason for this unusual privilege lies in Fort Logan's original charge to find new and nontraditional approaches to treatment, and without this privilege it seems unlikely that it would have been possible to develop a program where such a large active caseload could be handled with such a small number of beds. From the Fort Logan viewpoint, the selection took place not to deny its services to particular patients but rather to assure that treatment in a state facility was really necessary. "We felt that many patients could have been sent to us without there having been any reasonable exploration of community services that might have served just as well, and perhaps better, than we could," said Dr. Bonn.

In the early years the "refusal rate" sometimes ran as high as fifty percent, a circumstance that caused a certain amount of hard feeling toward Fort Logan. In more recent years, after the program became better established, there has been less stringent selection; there is at present some variation in practice among the treatment teams, and certain of them have begun to accept any patient referred to them by another treatment facility.

There are no categorical exclusions of patients except on the basis of age, and those who, by law, require maximum security. (Most alcoholics are also excluded from adult psychiatry, but approximately one thousand per year are treated by the alcoholism division.) Young people between the ages of 15 and 18 go to Colorado State Hospital, where there is a program for adolescents, which there is not at Fort Logan. There is some hope that the legislature will provide funds for such a program starting in mid-1969. Within Fort Logan, those under 15 are assigned to the children's unit, and the majority of patients over 65 go to the geriatric unit.

There are various differential criteria that operate to determine whether a new patient will be admitted to 24-hour or to day status, as described below.

Characteristics of the patients

Even though most of the patients in the adult psychiatry service are treated in a day program that is strikingly different from the treatment program of almost all state hospitals, the patients themselves have much in common with the usual state hospital population. The modal diagnosis is schizophrenia, which accounts for 36 percent of admissions. Other diagnoses are as follows:

Psychoneurotic reactions	15%
Personality disorders	7
Involutional psychotic reactions and psychotic depressive reactions	4
Chronic brain syndromes	2*
Alcoholism	2*
Manic-depressive reactions	1

The remaining 31 percent are not diagnosed at the time of admission; diagnosis is deferred pending further study by the psychiatrist. It is thought that the distribution among the deferred group is approximately the same as for those diagnosed at time of admission.

A little more than a third of those who were on day status during 1967 (490, or 36 percent) were men. The substantial majority of patients (91 percent) were between 21 and 65 years of age. Many had been previously hospitalized one or more times. The absolute number

---

*There are, of course, many more Fort Logan patients with chronic brain syndrome and with alcoholism than are indicated here. Most of them are admitted to the separate geriatric and alcoholism programs.

of readmissions to Fort Logan climbed from the time the facility opened in 1961. By 1965 it had reached 30 percent, where it has remained since. "We have no sympathy with the attitude that every readmission is a therapeutic failure," said Dr. Bonn. "Studies now under way are aimed at developing ways to differentiate readmissions into 'good' ones and 'failures.'"

Dr. Alan Kraft, when he was director of Fort Logan, prepared a paper* reporting the results of one of the very few systematic efforts we know of to determine the differential characteristics of persons admitted to day treatment and to 24-hour care. Although the study was done in 1962, during Fort Logan's second year, the staff believe that the findings continue to be applicable.

During the second half of 1962 the psychiatric teams admitted a total of 235 patients, of whom 49 percent were admitted as inpatients and 51 percent as day patients. Almost all of the inpatients moved rapidly to day status. During this period the patient ratio averaged one 24-hour patient to two and one-half day patients, and at any given time fewer than one third of all the patients in the two categories were inpatients.

Data processing cards were used to code a large amount of information about each patient. Of three hundred factors that were tabulated the staff chose fifty which were thought to show significant differences between patients admitted to day hospital and patients admitted to 24-hour care. Only fifteen of these factors were found to differentiate between the two groups, as follows:

Ratio of divorced and separated to married. More 24-hour patients came from broken marriages.

Voluntary vs. involuntary commitment. Involuntary commitments were necessarily admitted to 24-hour status; they comprised 35 percent of inpatient admissions and 17.5 percent of all psychiatric admissions.

Hallucinations. More of the 24-hour patients manifested hallucinations.

Impairment of effectiveness. A greater proportion of 24-hour patients were judged to be severely impaired by their illness.

Inappropriate behavior. A greater proportion of 24-hour patients exhibited inappropriate behavior.

Delusional thought content. A greater proportion of 24-hour patients manifested delusional thinking.

---

*A. Kraft: "Day Hospital Services as Part of an Integrated Psychiatric Treatment Program," in R. Epps and L. Hanes (eds.), *Day Care of Psychiatric Patients.* Charles C. Thomas, Springfield, Ill., 1964, pp. 79-90.

Disturbed orientation. Disorientation was more frequent among 24-hour patients.

Disturbance of alertness. Alterations in alertness were more frequent among 24-hour patients.

Confusion. The 24-hour patients were more confused than the day patients.

Concept of illness. A greater proportion of day patients had a fairly good understanding of their illness, or saw it as at least partly psychological rather than as a physical affliction or something caused by outside influences.

Personality disorganization. The 24-hour patients were judged to be more seriously disorganized.

Admission diagnosis. Eighty-three percent of 24-hour patients were diagnosed as psychotic or depressed, contrasted with 61 percent of the day patients. As for psychotic diagnoses alone, 76 percent of inpatients and 38 percent of day patients were so diagnosed.

Treatment just prior to admission. Persons admitted to 24-hour status were more often in treatment immediately prior to referral to Fort Logan.

Readmission to Fort Logan. Readmitted patients were more likely to be admitted as 24-hour patients.

Previous psychiatric treatment. A greater proportion of 24-hour admissions had previously been in treatment. However, 66 percent of day patient admissions had been treated previously as inpatients at some facility.

Obviously among these criteria there were various reasons why they proved to be differentiating. In any case it is valuable to have some information about what distinguishes the day patient from the 24-hour patient, particularly in a treatment facility where day treatment carries a strong positive value among all the staff. At the same time, it may be even more valuable to examine the characteristics that did not differentiate the two groups:

Age
Sex
Marital status (married vs. single)
Depressive thought content
Danger to self
Danger to others
Depressive affect
Previous suicide attempt
Previous suicide gesture

Intelligence
Prognosis
Distance of home from Fort Logan
Disturbance of relationship with family
History of difficulty with the law
Employed vs. unemployed

Dr. Kraft concluded that:

> . . . patients admitted to inpatient status are clearly more disturbed and more greatly impaired in their function than are the day patients. However, there are severely disturbed and impaired patients in both groups. . . .

> While our findings indicate some important differences between the two groups of patients, the dimensions along which they do not differ are equally important and striking. . . . Nationally there has been a growing dissatisfaction with the need to refer patients to inappropriate treatment facilities. Too frequently the choice lies between outpatient treatment and 24-hour inpatient treatment. With nothing in between, the choice becomes too much or not enough. We have found that when a day hospital is one of the choices available a large number of patients can make use of it.

Treatment philosophy

Fort Logan is acknowledged to be one of the outstanding and most highly developed examples of the therapeutic community. Says a brochure prepared by Fort Logan staff to describe its program to the public:

> Our therapeutic milieu, drawn heavily from the experience of Maxwell Jones, John and Elaine Cumming, Alfred Stanton, Morris Schwartz, and others, is based on the concept that all activities in a treatment day can potentially be used by the patient for strengthening of ego functions. The role of the staff is to maximize opportunities for the patient to learn from his experiences. The setting is manipulated so as to be protective, yet to provide a variety of situations from which the patient can benefit.

This is obviously a skeleton statement of the philosophy of the therapeutic community, a complex concept that can be understood only with much greater explication than is possible here. The authors have visited numerous treatment programs that call themselves "therapeutic communities" but in fact appear not to be, at least in that there is missing from them the role blurring, openness of communication, taboo against secrets or privileged communication, and constructive confrontation of inappropriate behavior. The Fort Logan program appears to have integrated these components of the therapeutic community into the very fabric of its program, and beyond this to have accrued important operating experience that sheds light on the effectiveness and the limitations of the therapeutic community. Those who have a serious interest in the therapeutic community would do well to see the Fort Logan program.

The acknowledgment of the worth of the patient is a cultural norm that permeates the program to a truly remarkable degree. Occasional staff behavior that has violated this norm has been met both by staff and by patients with incredulity.

Allied to the therapeutic community as a major philosophical underpinning is the pervasion of the need for continuity of care. Most mental illness is viewed by the Fort Logan staff as chronic illness carrying long-term impairment and requiring a variety of kinds and intensities of response at various phases. Continuity is built in not only by means of the combined day and inpatient programs but even more importantly by the fact that patients are assigned to treatment teams and not to services; consequently any person living in a particular neighborhood of Denver, for example, will be assigned to a treatment team that will serve him whether at a given time he is inpatient, day patient, or outpatient. Patients released without provision for further treatment are encouraged to contact Fort Logan if any further help should be needed.

"We did not anticipate a regular progression from inpatient to day hospital to outpatient," Dr. Bonn told us, "and fortunately so, because it rarely happens that way. Many of our patients move back and forth several times among the different intensities of treatment. The median length of stay in 1966-67 was 132 days overall, and during this period a given individual might conceivably be an inpatient, an outpatient, and a day patient two or more times each."

Treatment concepts have continued to evolve over the years—a disconcerting fact for some of those who return to Fort Logan after having grown enthusiastic about it as it was during its early days. As an example, an initial taboo on individual psychotherapy has been relaxed. "Our teams still do not use individual therapy extensively," said Dr. Bonn. "However, having given group treatment exhaustive applications during our earlier years, we would have been foolish to continue to refuse ever to use individual therapy after we had learned that there is a small number of patients at Fort Logan for whom group treatment alone is not sufficient. Furthermore, every patient needs relationships with individuals, staff and patients, and these are encouraged, but of course they are rigorously distinguished from formal psychotherapy."

Another change regards the accessibility of the sleeping areas during the day. In earlier years many of the treatment teams had absolutely forbidden inpatients to return to their rooms in the course of the day; with time this taboo was relaxed, out of the realization that an occasional patient may not be psychologically or physically equipped to participate in activities throughout the day.

The treatment program

Because of the latitude allowed the treatment teams in developing their individual programs, there is no uniform treatment schedule nor even a uniform list of activities in which all patients participate. Typically, a week will include several large group psychotherapy and community meeting sessions, most of which are followed by a half-hour staff review, one or more small group psychotherapy sessions, and psychodrama. In addition, most patient groups participate in work therapy, occupational therapy, recreation, social events, and home arts for periods ranging from one to three hours each.

There are free periods of time for "therapeutic exploitation" of the "daily living experience" during which "unstructured interaction between staff and patients" is encouraged. This activity is seen as essential to social learning, which the vast majority of the patients require at the most fundamental levels. Fort Logan feels that "staff must not fall back on structuring activities and schedules primarily for their own convenience or as a means of staying free of patient-staff interaction." Said Dr. Bonn, "We think perhaps the most important characteristic of the climate at Fort Logan is the predominantly friendly feeling between staff and patients, a feeling which we strive to achieve through clear communication of concern, respect, and compassion for one another."

Ordinarily the treatment day extends from 8:00 a.m. to 3:30 p.m. Most of the teams schedule one day a week to begin at noon and continue until 8:30 p.m., to provide an opportunity for relatives to participate. On this evening, typically, there will be a joint group therapy session for patients and relatives, a group therapy meeting involving the relatives alone, or a family unit therapy meeting. Sometimes the families also take part in the evening's recreational therapy.

Some of the teams have from time to time deliberately left a day of the week unscheduled, so that patients and staff can decide jointly, on the spot, what the patient group would like to do, and two of the teams use this approach on more than one day per week.

The authors spent varying amounts of time with different treatment teams observing the program and the interactions between staff and patients and between patients. The intensity of participation was impressive. There was extensive and quite open exploration of feelings. Many of the patients who had been treated in other types of hospitals appear to bring with them expectations of a program quite different from what they experience at Fort Logan, and a number of them have preconceived biases regarding the treatment capabilities of any staff members except physicians. These problems seemed to be dealt with expertly and openly. The sense of ease of communication and mutual respect among the staff members was impressive. Some patients expressed a desire for more individual contact and less group interaction with staff.

Medication. Substantially all Fort Logan patients receive moderate to heavy medication. This is administered at the patient's team unit by nursing staff. Day patients who require medication while at home pick it up from the Fort Logan pharmacy.

Regarding medication, Dr. Bonn told us, "One of the Joint Commission on Accreditation of Hospitals standards that requires updating is the present prohibition on self-medication by 24-hour hospital patients. To conform to this requirement, we cannot allow patients to keep medications on their persons or at the bedside. They must be distributed by the nurses, without exception. A more realistic approach would *a*) permit selected patients to have their own medication bottles in the locked medicine closet, from which, under supervision, they would get their prescribed dosage at the prescribed frequency, designated at easily remembered times; *b*) permit other selected patients to carry medications on their persons, to be taken without direct supervision. In this way, many patients could support the staff and each other in assuming responsibility for themselves and their treatment. The present stereotyped norm is destructive to the needs and capabilities of individual patients and is a key ingredient in the processes of dehumanization and institutionalization."

Disposition. Of 349 patients separated from partial hospitalization status during 1966-67, exactly three quarters were released without further provision for treatment. Eight percent were referred to private physicians for care, five percent were referred to outpatient services other than at Fort Logan, and six percent were transferred to various other hospitals.

During the same year another 455 day patients were transferred to outpatient status one or more times each. Another 106 moved from some other form of partial hospitalization to outpatient status.

Outcome. Approximately one third of day patients require transfer at some point, although often only briefly, to the inpatient service. Since the great majority of Fort Logan patients are severely ill and are considered both by referring agencies and by Fort Logan staff to require treatment by a state facility, this transfer rate appears reasonable. Furthermore, the figure includes those patients who were admitted on 24-hour status, transferred to day status, and then required transfer back to 24-hour status.

Transportation

Fort Logan's location at an extreme corner of Denver creates some commuting hardships. There is hourly bus service, but for persons who live at the far side of the city or in one of the outlying counties the trip can take well over an hour, and for many patients is prohibitively expensive. When we asked what changes would be desired if it were possible to plan the facility all over again at this point in time, we were told that the staff would prefer to have several smaller facilities dispersed throughout the catchment, rather than the one larger facility located at some distance from a great many of the people it serves.

Residential placements

Fort Logan operates a facility in downtown Denver as a residence for the placement of men who have been inpatients for at least a year. Called The Lodge, it has a capacity of fifteen; preference is given to schizophrenics. Expenses are met by funds from the Colorado Department of Rehabilitation and from collections from the residents.

Persons who have been inpatients can stay at one of Fort Logan's two halfway houses, which have a capacity of 32 patients each, for a month or longer, while concurrently looking for a job and attending day hospital, or while awaiting approval of an application for welfare funds.

Among approximately 85 patients in nursing homes and 80 in boarding homes are various persons who have been day patients. Group therapy, social group activities, and individual appointments are regularly provided there by the Fort Logan staff.

Job training and placement

About eighty percent of the day patients participate in the work therapy program. Its philosophy stems from the assumption that successful employment requires both technical or instrumental skills and socioemotional skills, and that many of the kinds of patients who are admitted to Fort Logan, even though they may have the instrumental skills, are likely to lack the socioemotional skills. Consequently the workshop emphasizes social structure "in which expectations are explicit and there is maximum opportunity to solve problems." The patients are paid on a piecework basis, but they are paid according to group rather than individual productivity, thereby bringing group norms and pressures into play.

There are full-time vocational counselors on each treatment team, providing daily contact with the patients, and a strong emphasis among all of the staff members on the patients' employment needs and potentials. Many patients have been placed in jobs, with limited success; one follow-up study indicated that more than ninety percent of the patients placed in jobs were not working one year later. This indicates to Fort Logan the need for a sheltered workshop in the community.

Financing

The Fort Logan budget is provided entirely by the State of Colorado. The charge to the patient is based upon his financial resources. The maximum for day care is $20 per day of attendance, which is substantially less than the actual cost. Only about three percent pay the full charge, and most of these payments come from health insurance or Medicare; 60 percent pay a reduced charge, and 37 percent pay nothing.

Future plans

Fort Logan intends to continue day hospital in all its treatment divisions and in mid-1968 was negotiating to arrange additional bus service from downtown Denver in order to accommodate as day patients some of the persons now requiring inpatient care or unable even to begin treatment because of transportation difficulties.

Funds for an adolescent treatment division are being requested from the legislature, to begin in 1969-70. It is anticipated that the day hospital will include schoolwork at Fort Logan and at schools in the community. There are plans to include more evening and weekend treatment for those in school in the community. Also, crisis intervention, involving the patient's family, will be emphasized.

The children's division is planning to train families to provide foster homes for children, thus allowing more utilization of day hospital.

Day hospital is one of the modalities that would be available in specialized programs being planned for drug addicts.

The extension of Fort Logan services into the community to date has involved the movement of one day hospital program (Adams County team) to a community clinic. Under contractual arrangements, other Fort Logan team staff are participating in other clinic-based day hospital programs. These are part of the three federally funded comprehensive centers, and a fourth such center in collaboration with Denver General Hospital is in process of development. Thus Fort Logan Mental Health Center is developing as a state hospital with four component subparts, each of which is a separate comprehensive community mental health center.

Additional day hospital programs, located in the community, are being considered for geriatric patients, alcoholic patients, and possibly several of the teams in the adult psychiatry division. Transportation problems and the advantages of a closer relationship with the community have stimulated such thinking. These considerations must be weighed against any potential additional costs and the impact of partial separation of staff and patients from those within Fort Logan. Stimulating other facilities and other agencies to develop such services would be an important part of Fort Logan's effort, as it has been in the past.

The evening hospital

Two of the teams have combined to operate a single evening hospital program. Both staff members and patients are drawn from the two teams, for a program that operates on Monday, Tuesday, and Thursday evenings. No patient is admitted to this program unless he is gainfully employed or attending school.

The hours are from 6:30 to 9:00 p.m., during which the patients participate in group psychotherapy, psychodrama, and recreation. On one evening per week family members are invited to participate.

The range of the census during fiscal 1967 was thirteen to twenty persons.

Psychiatric Day Center
Baltimore

THE PSYCHIATRIC DAY CENTER opened in October 1962 under the joint sponsorship of the Baltimore City Health Department and the Maryland State Department of Mental Hygiene. Located in downtown Baltimore, near the geographic center of the city, it is one of two facilities visited during this study which are freestanding and separate services rather than a service unit or program of a larger facility.* It has had the advantage of continuity of direction, under Dr. Gertrude Gross, who has developed a program that is an unusual and interesting intermix of medical direction and social rehabilitation. Dr. Gross considers the program to be a hospital in the full sense of the term. "Our patients are so sick that they must come to us every day, at least at the outset, and we maintain that persons with that degree of disorder should rightfully be considered as requiring the services of a hospital," she said. The program is called a "day center" only because of considerations of zoning regulations, which limit the term "hospital" to facilities having beds.

Physical plant

The day center occupies all of a row house on a main business street in an intown section of good quality. Two floors are used primarily by patients and two primarily by staff. In the basement are ample-sized rooms housing attractive art therapy and woodworking shops; on the second floor is a dayroom of adequate size for the usual attendance. The first and third floors are given over to a reception area, the director's office, a small pharmacy, and various small offices for the staff. Dr. Gross considers the total available space to be inadequate, and we shared her view that it would be desirable to have some additional space for patients. It is inconvenient and cumbersome both for staff and

---

*The other being the State Convalescent Center in Honolulu.

patients to have to negotiate three flights of stairs from the basement to the top floor. The general appearance is a bit Spartan, but patients and staff alike appear to feel that the setting is cheerful and homelike.

Capacity and range of census

From the outset the stated capacity of the program has been thirty patients, although this refers to the active caseload rather than the daily attendance. Dr. Gross believes that a day hospital should aim for a daily attendance of about twenty persons, about the ideal size both for classroom and for hospital ward. When the number goes much above this, she says, it becomes difficult to maintain the close personal patient-staff involvement; when it goes much below, it is difficult to maintain group process. Consequently, even if a larger physical plant and a larger staff were available, she would resist increasing the present patient load; instead, she believes, a second day hospital should be established. Furthermore, she thinks it is imperative that patients be scheduled for five days a week, at least initially; this program will not agree to take new patients at a lesser frequency.

During 1967 the daily attendance ranged from 12 to 22 persons. There were 52 different persons who attended during the course of a week in mid-January 1968; many of these in fact attended only one, two, or three days, but they were for the most part persons whose schedule had been reduced.

The staff

The ratio of staff to patients falls in the middle range of the programs we visited. It is, however, quite rich in terms of highly trained professionals. In addition to the full-time psychiatrist-director there is a half-time psychiatrist in the position of assistant director and there are two psychiatric residents spending half time each in the program. There are also a full-time and a half-time social worker, a full-time and a half-time registered nurse, a full-time aide, a full-time "therapeutic recreation specialist," and three half-time recreation aides. A psychologist spends a few hours a week in the program.

In terms of experience and training, there is a complete range within the staff. The psychiatrist-director spent ten years as admissions officer at one of Maryland's state hospitals, and the social workers and registered nurses have all had prior experience in psychiatric programs. Certain of the more successful aides, however, came to the program with no prior experience in a mental health facility. It appears evident that in this program, like most other high-quality programs that we know of, personal qualities of warmth and empathy are valued as much as professional credentials. We found it interesting to learn that a man who had retired from 23 years of service on the metropolitan police force had been brought into the program with particular success. Dr. Gross feels that the secretaries also play an important role; they set the tone for the facility, and often provide observations about patients and applicants that Dr. Gross considers useful in formulating the therapeutic approach to the individual. Programs that have pioneered in the use of the non-professional sometimes seem to feel compelled to deny the contribution of professional training; it was interesting to observe that the Baltimore program, one of the most medically oriented that we know of, had found it possible to incorporate nonprofessionals without in the least repudiating the competence of the professional. Each person on the staff seemed to strive to relate to patients in all aspects of the program, but the program responsibility of each staff member was limited to his own area of particular competence. (Consequently we were surprised to hear frequent mention of "role blurring"; for while there did not appear to be a hierarchy of personal worth, there was certainly a hierarchy of professional prerogatives and capabilities, and the typical connotation of "role blurring," as in the therapeutic community, did not seem to apply in this program.)

Homemaker service is available from the Family and Children's Society of Baltimore. At any given time there are from three to five women patients with small children for whom homemakers are provided, and without whose service it would not be possible for them to attend the day hospital.

We interviewed substantially all of the staff members, who appeared to be of high quality.

Volunteers are used to a total of about twelve hours per week. They provide transportation to take patients to and from outside activities, teach particular skills, and help with occasional small fund-raising projects.

Referrals and selection procedure

Maintaining a regular flow of appropriate referrals has been perhaps the most serious problem besetting this facility. To a large degree this situation is inherent in the program's concept of its mission. Because it attempts to serve only seriously disturbed patients in the acute phase of illness, it does not accept persons who are being discharged from inpatient care at the two state hospitals in the vicinity (nor does it need to, since each of these hospitals runs its own day treatment program). It must therefore rely on referrals from social agencies, hospital clinics, and physicians in private practice, particularly psychiatrists. The privately practicing psychiatrists account for the largest group of referrals, and such patients are usually one of four kinds: *a*) those who do not have the money to pay for private care, *b*) those who have had private outpatient care, did not respond, and appear to need a greater intensity of care, *c*) persons who, referred to psychiatrists for evaluation, are found to need intensive care and are then referred to the day hospital in preference to one of the state hospitals, and *d*) persons continuing in private therapy and in need of additional treatment.

Dr. Gross has found it necessary over the years to make periodic speeches and telephone calls inviting referrals. Even so, while the program accepts the sickest of the patients referred, not all of them are as severely disturbed as those the program prefers to treat.

The most important exclusion is, therefore, insufficient degree of pathology. "Of one hundred consecutive inquiries," Dr. Gross said, "we eliminate perhaps half just during the course of the telephone call. We don't simply turn these people away, however; when we have determined that they aren't for us we make a considerable effort to give them information that will help them to find an appropriate source of help. Of the remaining 50, perhaps 25 will actually come in for evaluation. Most of these will enter the program although some will drop out within the first week."

The only categorical exclusions are mental retardates, alcoholics, drug addicts, sociopaths, and uncontrolled epileptics.

There is a general policy that each patient must have an interested relative to live with. Exceptions have been made frequently. "The exceptions work out perhaps half the time," said Dr. DeWitt Weatherly, the assistant director.

Characteristics of the patients

Of 76 patients who were admitted to the program during 1967, more than half—42, or 55 percent—were persons with schizophrenic reaction. Exactly 25 percent, or 19 persons, were diagnosed as psychoneurotics, all of them with extremely disabling and impairing pathology, including severe phobic and compulsive symptoms. Psychotic depressions accounted for an additional eight percent, and the few remaining patients were divided among manic-depressive reactions, stress and adjustment reactions, and personality disorders.

About 70 percent of the patients were women. Substantially all (92 percent) were between 21 and 65 years of age. The considerable majority were considered to be of middle-class background.

Most of the patients have a moderate to lengthy history of mental illness. Many of them have been hospitalized in one of Maryland's state hospitals. Every one of them is viewed as a person who would, at the time of his entry into this program, require 24-hour hospitalization if the day hospital were not available.

Treatment philosophy

The treatment goals in this program are straightforward and sensible. Medication is used to stabilize the patient and reduce or eliminate symptoms. Psychotherapy is used to deal with the precipitating situational crisis, whether with family, employer, or something else. Activities are used to enhance socialization. Placements for jobs or job training are used to help the patient return to productive independent living.

Substantially all of the patients receive medication, in most cases in moderate to heavy dosage. "This is a basic underpinning of our program," said Dr. Gross. "Some of our staff people who have worked in other settings are astonished, when they come here, to see how many grossly psychotic people leave here to return to their jobs, principally maintained by medication. One of our main problems in referring our patients to private physicians for follow-up care is that these doctors too quickly reduce the dosage, or sometimes discontinue the medication altogether, usually at the patient's request, usually because of the financial burden.

"At the same time, we don't fool ourselves about the limits of usefulness of medication. It is fairly easy today to make symptoms disappear. But we consider this only the start. If a patient simply stops hallucinating and then goes home and sits in the corner and takes no part in family life or neighborhood life, we don't consider that we have accomplished very much. On the other hand, even if the patient still has paranoid ideas, it's all right with us provided he can be a part of his family and can hold a job."

Said Dr. Weatherly, "Medication is the first strength of the program, at least sequentially. Involvement with the patient's problems in living is the second. Each psychiatrist and resident conducts group therapy once a week, for a small group of patients, with either a social worker or nurse serving as co-therapist. We use the group to explore with the patients the problems that are troubling them, both here at the center and at home. After the group session is over the co-therapist and the psychiatrist discuss what we think is going on with the patients. If it seems appropriate, the social worker schedules an appointment with a member of the patient's family. When the relative comes in, the social worker, the patient, the relative, and the doctor all meet together. These group and individual contacts are the means whereby we become familiar with and stay abreast of the patient's problems and plot what changes are needed to help him survive outside of a 24-hour hospital."

Most of the patients accepted in this program are in a state of decompensation, and many of them are desocialized as well. The activity groups foster interaction designed to increase social capabilities. During the coffee hour that starts the day, patients are not allowed, for instance, to read newspapers or knit, but instead are encouraged to engage in conversation with the staff and with fellow patients. Participation in group activities is said to be mandatory, although in reality the favorable staffing ratio makes it possible in most cases to persuade, rather than to order, patients to participate.

The groups serve an added purpose, in the view of Sandra Philip, the therapeutic recreation specialist. "What to do with an increasing amount of leisure time is increasingly a problem for almost everyone in our society," she said, "but particularly so for people who are ill or disabled. We try to teach a variety of skills, so that when our patients no longer need to come here they will be capable of participating in activities in the community. Some of them are so chronically ill that they probably never will make it on the outside without special support, so we refer them to agencies such as the Metropolitan Baltimore Association for Mental Health, which sponsors social activities for mentally ill people living in the community."

Said Dr. Weatherly, "The art work is designed to invite freedom of expression and internal feelings and the shop area is set up to give the patient some project to follow through to completion. All the while, we emphasize and encourage conversation."

The ability to return to work, or begin work, is the goal for a number of patients. Even though the majority of patients are women, many of them are in need of employment for a variety of reasons, and the program places major emphasis on obtaining the services necessary to enable them to return to work or to begin work.

The treatment program

The regular program within the day hospital is limited to the components described above: medication, group therapy conducted by a psychiatrist, and therapeutic recreation. Individual interviews and home visits supplement this regimen in indicated cases.

The program operates five days a week, from 9:30 a.m. to 3:30 p.m. Until ten o'clock the patients and staff engage in a coffee hour, the principal purpose of which is to encourage group conversation. Medications are dispensed by the nurses during this time. At ten o'clock the group breaks up into smaller units, usually three, and the following two hours is spent in such activities as woodworking, art work, and needlecrafts. The weekly group therapy sessions also take place during this morning period.

The patients bring their own lunches, and they eat together in the dayroom, accompanied by one or more staff members, while the rest of the staff eat lunch separately, utilizing this time to discuss problems of particular patients. After lunch and until three o'clock the patients resume small-group activities, in most cases switching to an activity different from that of the morning period. There are regularly scheduled field trips, including trips to a nearby bowling alley and to an indoor swimming pool. Shortly after three o'clock the patients assemble in the dayroom for afternoon medication. Housekeeping chores are done during the remaining few minutes, and all of the patients leave at three thirty. During the following hour the staff meet again to resolve any problems.

Because of the strong emphasis on enabling the patient to participate in activities outside of the program, tickets for sporting and cultural events are solicited by staff members. "We try to take into account what the patient has been interested in, rather than steer him to something alien to his interests," said Miss Philip. "More often than not we give several tickets to a patient and his family rather than to a group of patients, because this encourages him and his relatives to share experiences that we hope will foster good feelings among them.

"We regularly take trips during the day, too. A typical example would be for one or more staff members to accompany six or seven of our women to have lunch at a department store, and then go shopping afterwards. If we have patients who are unable to ride buses, we set up an activity that involves a bus ride."

The consultants were impressed with the neat and attractive appearance of the patients. "We stress appearance particularly," Dr. Gross said. "We have a hair dryer here and we encourage the women to use it, and sometimes we help them with it. We tell the patients that if they come here looking tattered and bedraggled that it shows a lack of respect not only for themselves but for their fellow patients and for the staff."

Work-for-pay. This program has undertaken no work-for-pay projects. Because of the limited space available, it probably would not be possible to do so.

Boarding. It is not possible under any circumstances to arrange temporary inpatient boarding for a disturbed day patient, nor has the program been able to avail itself of emergency coverage for nights and weekends. Typically a day hospital patient who becomes grossly disturbed would have to be eliminated from the program and hospitalized under other auspices, most likely at a state hospital. The fact that the program is not backed up by an emergency service has undoubtedly had a major influence on the kind of patient it accepts. This has also undoubtedly influenced the various sources that are looked to for referrals.

Disposition and outcome. Of 88 patients separated from the program during 1967, eight (nine percent) were transferred to inpatient treatment. This appears to be a low figure compared to the majority of day hospitals that we visited, particularly so in view of the characteristics of this patient population. About three fifths of the 88 patients were considered to be "improved," 30 percent were considered "unimproved." and eight percent left the program against medical advice.

Aftercare. One of the most interesting aspects of this program is an aftercare clinic that developed not by plan but in response to need. Soon after the day center opened it became evident that many of the patients who no longer needed to attend did, however, require continued medication. Referral to private physicians was often unsatisfactory, since the patient, finding it a burden to pay as much as $25 to $30 per month for prescription drugs, urged the physician to cut back on medication, with the result that symptoms returned and decompensation set in.

The day center thereupon began individually and informally to schedule return appointments for patients to check their medication and to provide an additional supply. (Day center patients who have been patients at one of the state hospitals can avail themselves of the aftercare clinics which these hospitals operate in Baltimore. But many will not do so, because of their concern that any show of returning symptoms might result in their being returned to the state hospital.) This unprogrammed and unbudgeted aftercare grew to the point that the center now devotes one afternoon each week to it. On Thursday afternoons the regular program is suspended. A number of ex-patients, usually ten to twelve, come at one thirty to meet with the staff. Each patient is seen for ten or fifteen minutes by one of the psychiatrists, at which time it is determined whether the patient should continue on the same dosage of the same medication or whether a change is called for. Then the patient reports to one of the nurses, who dispenses the indicated medication. These drugs are charged at cost, plus a two percent markup, if the patient can afford it. If not, a sliding fee scale is used, with some patients paying nothing. Most patients also spend some time with various other members of the staff.

Typically a patient just released from the program is scheduled for a follow-up appointment two weeks later, and thereafter at an interval of six, eight, or ten weeks. Thus, with ten to twelve patients being seen each Thursday, there are altogether about eighty patients in the aftercare program.

It is made clear to each person that he is free to telephone for help between appointments if this should be necessary. Two such calls were received during our visit, and we were impressed with the immediacy of response and the extent of involvement with each patient's problem.

Transportation

The day center is conveniently located, as urban transit systems go. Accessibility by public transportation has not been an important problem.

Job placements

Patients who need evaluation and/or placement for jobs can readily obtain service from the Division of Vocational Rehabilitation. A counselor who works full time with psychiatric patients has this program among his designated assignments. The number of cases involved is small. Most often he arranges with the Metropolitan Baltimore Association for Mental Health to enroll the patient in a work-sample program that takes place entirely within the association's offices but provides a variety of activities.

Dr. Gross and her staff have individually persuaded employers to take back employees who have been treated in the day hospital. There has been particular success with one of Baltimore's largest department stores, which not only accepts back its own employees but has hired several other patients in new jobs.

Financing

Substantially all of the costs of the program have been met from public funds, under an interesting arrangement whereby the Maryland Department of Mental Hygiene provides half of the funds and the Baltimore City Health Department the remaining half (although half of the city funds in fact come from matching funds provided by the State Health Department).

There is a sliding scale of fees based on income and size of family, with a range from fifty cents to $47.50 per week. An effort is made to establish a weekly minimum charge of $5 and most of the patients do pay this amount. Very few pay more than $10 per week.

Because the day hospital does not meet the various legal requirements that define a "hospital," patients are not eligible for reimbursement under most health insurance policies, including Blue Cross and Blue Shield.

Future plans

This day hospital has joined forces with North Charles General Hospital, a nearby general hospital, in applying for federal funds to develop a community mental health center. Assuming that the grant becomes effective and that the program develops as anticipated, psychiatric beds will then be available for the first time in Baltimore in a voluntary general hospital that is not part of a training program. The day hospital will be relocated into the physical plant of the general hospital, in part because the lease on the present premises is about to expire and in part because the present physical plant is not considered adequate. It will be interesting to see what effect the new and quite different physical setting will have on the characteristics of the program. Dr. Gross sees the ready availability of emergency service as the principal advantage that the new arrangement will have for the day hospital itself.

Lincoln Hospital Mental Health Services
Bronx, New York

D IRECTED BY Dr. Harris B. Peck, the mental health services provided at Lincoln Hospital, one of New York City's public general hospitals, consist of an imaginative and broad program that is richly staffed with skillful, well-trained personnel. Dr. Seymour Kaplan, associate director in charge of clinical programs, maintains that the Lincoln partial hospitalization services provide two interrelated though physically separated treatment programs. One is a traditional day hospital (to the extent that any day hospital can yet be said to be traditional), and the other is an "Intensive Care" treatment program that provides care for many patients who require more extensive attention than is usually provided by an outpatient service but who do not require inpatient or day hospital care. This latter service model evolved from the participation of the directors of the Lincoln Hospital Mental Health Services and their associates in the partial hospitalization research done early in this decade at Westchester Square in the Bronx.

The auspices

Lincoln Hospital's mental health program, affiliated with the well-known program of the Albert Einstein College of Medicine, began in 1963, in a dilapidated hospital that was extensively remodeled but still presents an appearance of impoverishment. This hospital is located in the South Bronx, in an extremely depressed area now populated principally by poor Negroes and Puerto Ricans. The incidence of social pathology is considerably greater than that for New York City as a whole, and is among the most severe in any urban ghetto in the nation. Mobility both into and out of the neighborhood and within it is extremely high.

From a small initial start the program has grown rapidly, so that today it has about 200 personnel, of whom about 75 are professionals and 50 are nonprofessional mental health workers ("indigenous nonprofessionals") who are selected and trained by the program and are one of its highlights. Other personnel are employed in the program's research and evaluation unit.

Fairly early three neighborhood service centers, popularly known as "storefronts," were established and staffed with nonprofessional mental health workers. The function of these centers is to help troubled poor people who live in the immediate vicinity, principally by helping them to find their way through a network of community services and agencies which they are relatively incapable of dealing with unassisted.

This program sees its role as one of providing an array of services that will prevent hospitalization. The staff appeared to us to view the neighborhood service centers as a means of primary prevention of mental illness through community service and organization. The treatment services at Lincoln Hospital tend to be focused more upon secondary and tertiary prevention.*

There are two major entry points into the system: the emergency room at Lincoln Hospital, where at all times psychiatric staff are available immediately on call, and the mental hygiene "walk in" clinic at Lincoln Hospital which operates from 8:30 a.m. to 4:30 p.m. Monday through Friday and provides prompt attention to "walk in" patients.

Administratively this program is one of the most complicated that any of the authors have encountered. For one thing, the mental health service has no inpatient service; instead, eight wards of forty beds each at the Bronx State Hospital are designated for the area served by Lincoln. For another thing, the area which the hospital serves has been subdivided into an Area A, having about 250,000 persons, and an Area B, having about 100,000. This split was made for several reasons, including principally *a*) the belief that service could be more effectively provided to two smaller units, *b*) to facilitate in the smaller area various research projects that have been planned in conjunction with a federal staffing grant request to develop a community mental health center, and *c*) to comply with federal regulations that require a clear separation between the population to be served in the projected community mental health center area (with a maximum of 200,000) and the population served in other areas. Therefore, the services provided by Areas A and B, even though they are ultimately under the same direction, are not identical. As an example, the "traditional" day hospital referred to above serves only Area B patients, and there is no day hospital in the cus-

---

*During late 1968 this model of services was altered with the implementation of the Lincoln Hospital Community Mental Health Center. The center includes two neighborhood mental health units which combine elements of the neighborhood service centers along with clinical services and expanded consultation and education programs.

tomary sense for Area A. It is pointless in this context to burden the reader with the intricacies of this structure and its interrelationships, and instead only aspects pertinent to the partial hospitalization services will be mentioned, and then at the necessary point in the description of those services.

It is important to note that this highly publicized service appears to have a highly developed sense of mission to the area it serves, and that its accomplishments in training neighborhood nonprofessionals provide important experience applicable to the future delivery of all public mental health services in this country. The extreme richness of staffing, however, diminishes the extent to which this program can be considered as a model for other parts of the country.

I. "INTENSIVE CARE"

The term "Intensive Care" is used in most medical facilities to denote an inpatient program in which every suitable mode of treatment is brought to bear in the hope of effecting a favorable outcome for critically ill persons. In the Lincoln Hospital Mental Health Services, it is used to denote a service that many persons, including the authors, would be inclined to consider an elaborate form of outpatient service but which the Lincoln staff prefer to consider a refinement of partial hospitalization.

In any case, the program appears to keep a number of severely disturbed persons functioning in the community by means of providing them an exposure to mental health services for periods ranging from two to nine hours per week. Drs. Peck and Kaplan therefore hold that the program is a form of partial hospitalization. (It is pertinent here to recall that partial hospitalization is not nearly so much an "all or none" proposition as persons unfamiliar with actual programs are inclined to suppose. In the typical day hospital program, no more than half of the active caseload attend on a given day. There are oftentimes as many persons scheduled to come only one or two days a week as there are scheduled to come five days a week.)

It is the latter arrangement that prevails in the Intensive Care service at Lincoln. The service provides individual and group services. At the time of our visit there were nine groups, each having an active membership ranging from ten to thirty. These groups meet one, two, or three times per week each. Among them are strictly verbal discussion groups, strictly activity groups including a work-for-pay program, and various combinations of these. A typical group may meet on a Tuesday afternoon for two hours of group therapy led by a psychiatrist, psychologist, or social worker and with a mental health worker as adjunct group leader, and on a Friday morning for three hours of group work-for-pay activity. Drs. Peck and Kaplan maintain that this level of involvement is sufficient for many persons who in other programs are admitted as inpatients.

Capacity and range of census

The average daily census for all nine of the Intensive Care groups combined during 1967 was reported to be 37. During the week of January 15, 1968, a total of 75 persons participated in these groups. The overall active caseload during the year was reported to be 150.

Physical plant

The quarters available to the Intensive Care service consist of a waiting area, thirteen private offices, and two group treatment rooms, all located in the Lincoln Hospital, and an activity area located in a converted factory loft two blocks away. The facilities are cramped, overtaxed, and generally inadequate.

The staff

About one third of staff time for the treatment teams assigned to Areas A and B is devoted to the individual and group services that make up the Intensive Care program. These include five psychiatrists, four psychologists, a social worker, an art therapist, and seven community mental health workers. There are also three first-year residents.

We were favorably impressed with the two mental health workers selected for us to interview. They may well have been the cream of the crop; certainly they appeared to be extremely capable, warm, empathic, and interested in patients, with verbal fluency and pride in their accomplishments.* The program went to great lengths to recruit and screen applicants for the mental health worker positions. Each person chosen was given training ranging from five weeks upward, depending on the program to which he was to be assigned. There is continuing inservice training and supervision. The Spanish-speaking mental health workers spend a good share of their time as interpreters, and it was interesting to see the evidence of the pride in their usefulness in this capacity. One of them described an interesting dilemma. Early in his experience, when patients spoke in an obscene or disorganized fashion, he felt the need to make them sound better in translation, so

---

*Both have since left to accept better-paying jobs.

as to protect both the staff and the patients from embarrassment. Later he learned to sound "as crazy as possible" so that the professional staff could better understand the patients' thought processes and feelings.

Another role in which mental health workers take considerable pride is as "expeditors." In this line they help patients obtain assistance from welfare and vocational rehabilitation services, and otherwise assist patients in activities that require interaction with agencies and parts of the community that they are unfamiliar with. Apparently the ethnic groups in this catchment commonly experience despair, futility, and impotence in coping with the white establishment, and the mental health workers are determined to help them to get what they need. They see themselves as serving as models for the patients, by demonstrating how to talk and how to deal with recalcitrant community resources. They feel that their major contribution is to show the patient that he can do it himself, and consequently they provide only that degree of guidance and support necessary for the patient to do it himself.

A major question surrounds the future of these young people. They themselves ask, "Where do we go from here?" While evidencing growing pride and awareness of their own capabilities, they are concerned about limited opportunities for recognition and financial betterment. It remains to be seen whether over any extended period of time a career as a "subprofessional" can be satisfying for these articulate and warm persons. (Since the time of our visit a special educational benefit clause was added to the union contract which covers all the community mental health workers at Lincoln Hospital. Under this provision a community mental health worker can receive up to fifteen hours a week off for attending classes with all tuition paid.)

Referrals

The referral patterns within the Lincoln Hospital Mental Health Services and its affiliate services are so complicated that figures were not available indicating the various sources from which the 150 active cases in Intensive Care had come. They are probably not greatly different from the total referrals of all active cases being seen in any element of care (except for a higher percentage of emergency room referrals), specifically: from medical services other than Lincoln Hospital, 28 percent; from the Lincoln Hospital emergency room, 22 percent; self-referrals, 19 percent; from various community services, 17 percent; from within Lincoln Hospital other than the emergency room, 14 percent.

Selection procedure

The principal determinant of eligibility for Intensive Care is whether the patient is suffering from an acute or subacute psychiatric disorder and can be maintained with contact of a few hours per week. Persons who require 24-hour medical-surgical care or whose clinical symptoms are too severe to be handled on any other than an inpatient basis are obviously not accepted.

Characteristics of the patients

We have mentioned that these patients are among the most deprived in any of the urban areas of the United States. A little over half of them are Spanish-speaking and comprise the least privileged of New York's Puerto Rican population. Some are newly arrived, but more are persons who "commute" between New York and Puerto Rico, spending a few months here, a few months there. Many of the Negroes are recent arrivals from the South.

About three quarters of the patients are women. About ninety percent are between 21 and 65 years old, and of the remaining ten percent, more are over 65 than under 21. More than half have a history of hospitalization for mental illness.

Schizophrenia is by far the largest diagnostic category (77 percent), followed by psychoneurosis (15 percent), and psychotic depression (three percent), with all other diagnoses accounting for five percent.

Treatment philosophy

Said Dr. Peck, "We have a mandate to help reduce the hospitalized population in the Bronx, and consequently we focus on the disturbed patient during the acute and subacute phase. Our goal is to emphasize follow-up care, right from the moment the person enters our system, and our objective is to consider how a follow-up arrangement can be accomplished for him. We are convinced that without adequate follow-up arrangements there will be no significant decrease in hospitalization rates. Consequently, we provide a brief but intensive involvement, with a tapering off of patient visits according to the nature of the clinical problem.

"We are focusing on the psychotic patient. If one wants to take care of sociopaths and other character disorders, he must have a facility that can provide six months or more of care, in which there can be a deep therapeutic involvement, and that is beyond our present resources."

Dr. Kaplan appears to be concerned most of all with the fragmentation that has characterized mental illness services (and all medical services, he maintains). "For the psychotic patient, continuity of care is the critical challenge," he says. "Any fundamental alteration in the course of illness for most psychotic patients depends on the type, quality, and quantity of prehospital and posthospital care. Partial hospitalization services can help not merely as a substitute for full-time inpatient care but also as an urgently needed form of transitional care."

The treatment program

Both individual and group psychotherapy are prescribed for most of the Intensive Care patients. However, the term "individual psychotherapy" as applied here requires examination. While most of the patients are seen at some time during their course of treatment, most often in the early phase, in individual appointments lasting from twenty to sixty minutes, those appointments rarely focus on internal problems. "Patients from this area are not used to psychologizing," we were told. "They don't verbalize that they feel nervous this morning because of some childhood experience, or that they feel a vague sense of dread because they don't know what their purpose and destiny is. Yet many of them are quite verbal. By and large we don't feel that intrapersonal and intrapsychic approaches are appropriate for psychotic patients during the acute or subacute phase of the illness. Furthermore, because of special aspects of the social and cultural conditions of the patients we see, we have found that the most effective way to facilitate reconstitution of ego-functioning is in a group setting. Consequently, we tend to emphasize group treatment approaches as soon as possible. However, it is necessary for individual contact with a therapist to be maintained at the outset for about four to fifteen appointments and for the therapist to be available for individual meetings with the patient from time to time thereafter. It is important for the patient to know that a single individual is responsible for managing and directing the treatment. In reality, 'individual contact' would be a more accurate term than 'individual psychotherapy.' "

It is important to point out the role that the mental health worker plays in the success of this treatment approach. At the outset the professional therapist and the medication he provides are often the primary focus of the patient's emotional needs. However, the mental health worker, who provides many of the adjunct services already discussed, gradually assumes larger meaning to the patient and often is the most significant staff person who maintains continuity with him during the recovery phase of his illness.

The work-for-pay program, with participation usually limited to two or three hours a week for each patient, is one of the important group activities that along with group discussion periods form the group treatment program. The work-for-pay program consists of light assembly work that is contracted for from private industry and for which patients are remunerated forty cents an hour. Most of the work is arranged for by Altro Work Shops, Inc. and subcontracted to the Lincoln Hospital Mental Health Services. Occasionally work contracts are arranged for independently by the Lincoln staff.

Other activities besides a formal work project are used. Patients are encouraged to suggest projects. As an example, we were told of a project that originated with a patient who was a cabinetmaker. The group decided to take an assortment of old chairs, sand them down and paint them, then use them in the various offices and meeting rooms. The project went on for about six weeks, with the patients coming in two afternoons a week. "In the beginning," said one of the mental health workers, "everything bothered them—the smell of paint and benzine, for example. But when I began working with them as if I were a foreman, it turned into a factory kind of setup, with one man who wasn't bothered by paint doing the painting, another doing the sanding, and so on. The more I worked, the more the patients tried to follow my pace. When it was all finished, everybody took a lot of satisfaction in seeing the chairs in the waiting room and down in the auditorium."

Medication. Up to ninety percent of the Intensive Care patients receive some psychotropic medication. The psychiatrist involved in the treatment prescribes the medication, which is dispensed at the Lincoln Hospital outpatient pharmacy at no charge to the patient. Where a nonmedical person is the therapist, the prescription of medication is supervised by a psychiatrist.

Boarding. There are five overnight beds available in the partial hospitalization unit which can be used to hold a patient for 24 to 72 hours. If a longer time is required, hospitalization at the Lincoln Unit of Bronx State Hospital is arranged, in which case an early return to the Lincoln Hospital Mental Health Services is often possible.

Home visits. Mental health workers make home visits when indicated. These may be for such things as assessment of home environment, encouraging patients to continue treatment, and facilitating homemaker services.

Disposition. Most patients in the Intensive Care unit are followed in the general outpatient clinic of Lincoln Hospital after remission of acute symptoms. The chart is not closed nor a formal transfer made. Statistics were not available for patients so followed or who have required transfer to inpatient services.

Outcome. Outcome studies have not been made of Intensive Care patients.

Transportation

Lincoln Hospital is located at the periphery of the area it serves. A number of partial hospitalization patients take the bus. For welfare clients bus fare is paid by the welfare department; these payments are sometimes delayed, and staff members sometimes loan bus fare to patients awaiting welfare funds.

Agency relationships

There is no formal liaison with public agencies involved with welfare and housing. However, there is a very active, even if informal, collaboration with them. The mental health workers are especially effective in this area. Vocational rehabilitation services are both provided by and implemented with other agencies through Lincoln's own vocational rehabilitation department. There are formal liaison relationships with the Visiting Nurse Service and with most of the "group-serving" agencies in the area and with many churches that provide social and recreational resources for the patients.

Placements

There are no formal placement arrangements. However, there is active collaboration with the social service department that provides such services. There are plans to develop a foster home placement program. With regard to job placement, some mental health workers have in individual cases demonstrated particular skills in arranging jobs for patients.

Financing

Patients in the Intensive Care program are classified as clinic patients and thus, under existing regulations in New York City, are not assessed any fee at all. Operating funds for the program are provided through a contract between the Community Mental Health Board of New York City and the Albert Einstein College of Medicine of Yeshiva University. All mental health funds contracted by the Community Mental Health Board of New York City have a fifty percent matching basis with New York State.

Future plans

It is now planned to expand the Intensive Care program in order to provide a greater range of therapeutic services, including more frequent and prolonged group treatment and open workshops. A major emphasis will be to improve the administrative structure so that patient flow between the various facilities can be more effectively consolidated. The addition of the five overnight beds along with appropriate management of current resources should allow for a still greater decrease in admissions to the beds at Bronx State Hospital, which for the past year was twenty percent lower than for the previous year. The research department has been awarded a grant from the National Institute of Mental Health, including funds for an evaluation study. A greatly expanded record-keeping system with a computerized data bank is being installed as a first step in the evaluation and outcome studies.

II. THE DAY HOSPITAL

The day hospital, serving only Area B, was established in October 1966. It has a capacity of 25 patients. In a typical week about twenty persons attend, fairly evenly distributed by number of days per week.

At the time of our visit the day hospital was located in an upper story of a manufacturing loft, about two blocks from the hospital, in makeshift facilities. There was a dayroom of ample size, some activity rooms, and limited office space. This temporary arrangement was superseded in late April 1968 when the program moved back into the Lincoln Hospital, into small but reasonably adequate renovated quarters. There are several meeting rooms and offices available, and for the first time there are five beds that may be used for holding patients who may require inpatient care for 24 to 72 hours. The use of these beds is shared with the Intensive Care service.

The program operates five days a week, from 9 a.m. to 4 p.m.

The full-time staff consist of a psychiatrist-administrator, three registered nurses, and five community mental health workers. An art therapist and an industrial therapist spend a few hours a week each in the program. The first-year residents mentioned above as part of the Intensive Care staff spend some of their time in this day hospital.

The staff for the overnight service consist of three nurses and six mental health workers. The psychiatrist on duty at the emergency room covers this service. The overnight service is available every night including weekends.

One volunteer had taught some classes in the past, but there was no volunteer activity at the time of our visit.

Referrals

The majority of patients come on referral from the Lincoln Hospital emergency room, where they will have been seen one or two times. If they are first seen at night or on a weekend, it is the night psychiatrist who holds them at the emergency room or sends them home on the assurance that they will return when the day hospital is open. There are about six new patients per month from this source. The other major source of patients is referral from other elements of the Lincoln Hospital Mental Health Services, usually at the request of particular therapists. An occasional patient is referred from the Lincoln Unit of Bronx State Hospital for transitional care prior to return to his family.

Selection procedure

The psychiatrist-administrator, Dr. James Finkelstein, decides in most cases whether a patient referred for day hospital is suitable for his program. A number of situational criteria are put forth:

• The patient must be sixteen years of age or older.
• He must not be suffering from alcoholism nor be addicted to narcotics.
• He must not have 24-hour medical-surgical needs.
• He must be able to travel by himself or have someone available to transport him.
• His clinical symptoms must not be too severe to be managed at home at night and on weekends.
• His relationship to his family must not be so destructive as to indicate complete separation from home.
• The patient's family must be willing to have him live there.
• The patient must not be under any form of commitment or on any legal status calling for 24-hour care.

Additionally, Dr. Finkelstein makes a clinical determination. "In a typical case," he said, "the emergency room will call me to say that there's a patient there who seems suitable for the day hospital. I see him, then I decide. Frankly, I don't always know what tips the decision in one direction or the other. Certainly we take people of extreme degrees of psychotic decompensation and manage to hold them pretty well. I suppose the criteria after all come down to the patient's situation."

Characteristics of the patients

During 1967 a total of 96 patients were seen in the day hospital, of whom 15 were admitted for two or more periods. There were about twice as many women as men. About 90 percent of the patients were between 21 and 65, and all of the rest were under 21. By far the largest diagnosis was schizophrenic reactions (49 percent), followed by psychotic depressions (26 percent). Psychophysiologic reactions accounted for ten percent and personality disorders for seven percent.

"The patients we get," Dr. Finkelstein said, "seem to be those that our therapists consider to be too ill to be maintained without substantial contact with the program. Comparing our diagnoses with those of Intensive Care, we have a larger group of affective disorders, many of whom present the possibility of suicide. We also get a lot of patients who have young children; the mother is known to leave her child alone in a bad apartment in a bad neighborhood. The therapists may send the patient to us because we have a proportionately higher number of mental health workers in our unit who are available to go to the home and who have the time to arrange for day care or nursery school for the children."

The treatment program

Dr. Finkelstein sees the structure of the day program as the most important component of treatment. It is the structure that provides the patient with a sense of belonging to a group. Interestingly, the day begins with group preparation of breakfast, a simple act that provides both nutritional and psychological advantages.

"A great deal of what the patient gets in this program he gets through the breakfast and lunch preparation and the informal socialization that goes on throughout the day," Dr. Finkelstein said. "Many positive things have happened between patients; friendship groups have developed, and some romances. The staff and community mental health workers have become involved in various kinds of social relationships with patients outside the day hospital."

About 85 percent of the day patients are on psychotropic medications, dispensed by the nurses during the day. All patients take part in occupational therapy and recreation activities in the day hospital unit. Some patients participate in the group treatment program of the overall Lincoln service including the work-for-pay program. All patients participate in the daily group therapy sessions in the day hospital. Selected patients are seen in individual therapy by the professional staff.

During a typical day, the first hour is used in preparing and eating breakfast, and cleaning up afterward. Then comes a half-hour of free time, followed by an hour-and-a-half group therapy session—the first 45 minutes with the psychiatrist, the second with the psychiatric nurse. Lunch is prepared and served, and the kitchen area cleaned, after which there is a patient government or other type of community meeting, followed by work-for-pay, occupational therapy, recreational therapy, or other organized activity. At four o'clock the patients leave. The staff then hold a half-hour meeting.

Home visits. Mental health workers make home visits to assess the home environment, to help a patient return to the hospital, to arrange for day care or nursery school for patients' children, and so on.

Disposition. During 1967, it became necessary to transfer to inpatient status a total of twelve out of 111 admissions. Other disposition figures were not furnished.

Outcome. Data on outcome of treatment were not available.

Agency relationships

There is no formal liaison with public agencies involved with welfare and housing. However, there is a very active collaboration with them on an informal basis. The mental health workers are especially effective in this area. Vocational rehabilitation services are both provided by and implemented with other agencies through the Lincoln Hospital Mental Health Services' vocational rehabilitation department. Formal liaison relationships exist with the Visiting Nurse Service and with most of the group-serving agencies in the area and with many churches that provide social and recreational resources for the patients.

Placements

There are no formal placement arrangements. However, there is active collaboration with the social service department that provides such services. There are plans to develop a foster home placement program. With regard to job placement, some mental health workers have in individual cases demonstrated particular skills in arranging jobs for patients.

Financing

No fees are levied for this program. All funds have been furnished through a contract between the Community Mental Health Board of New York City and the Albert Einstein College of Medicine of Yeshiva University.

Future plans

The development of the day hospital is intricately tied up with the overall development of partial hospitalization services including the Intensive Care service. A closer tie-in with the overall Lincoln Hospital Mental Health Services to provide continuity of care is a first objective. Expansion of services now made available by the overnight beds will also include development of an evening and weekend program.

Temple University Community Mental Health Center
Philadelphia

THE TEMPLE UNIVERSITY Community Mental Health Center came into being in mid-1966 and began accepting patients in early 1967. It consists of an emergency service called the Crisis Center; an outpatient service called the Psychosocial Clinic staffed mainly by "indigenous" mental health workers; a 15-bed inpatient service located in the Temple University Hospital and an 85-bed inpatient service located in Philadelphia State Hospital; the Social Adjustment and Rehabilitation Unit, which emphasizes vocational and educational activities; a Children's and Family Service; partial hospitalization services consisting of a day and an evening-night program; a consultation and education program; and a research and evaluation unit. Although at the time of our visit the mental health center was still very much evolving, it appeared to be a healthy program that was making a major effort to provide a broad spectrum of service to its catchment, which consists of an impoverished portion of North Philadelphia with a population of 215,000. The residents are mainly Negro. The unemployment and welfare rates are very high.

The partial hospitalization service is not an entry point into the program and must depend on other components for referrals. It operates with very substantial autonomy, under the direction of Dr. Frederick Glaser, a young psychiatrist who impressed us as committed and well trained. With the support of Dr. Elmer Gardner, director of the mental health center, Dr. Glaser has developed a well-thought-out program that can truly be called a therapeutic community, with major emphasis on socialization. We shall concentrate here on the day program.

Capacity and range of census

The day program had been open barely six months at the time of our visit in mid-March 1968. The indicated capacity at that time was "30 plus." During its first three months the program had a census ranging up to 22, and during the first three months of 1968 from 15 to 33. The attendance on the day of our visit was 21, about two thirds of the active caseload at that time and consequently a slightly higher proportion than in most of the other programs we visited. The program operates Monday through Friday, from 9:30 a.m. until 5:00 p.m.

Physical plant

The program takes place in a "double house" near Temple University Hospital, in a somewhat dilapidated, primarily residential area. The two internally connected row houses were formerly used to house residents from the medical school. They were structurally altered and have been modestly but pleasantly furnished. The first floor has an enclosed porch, a reception office, a gathering room with several small tables where coffee and snacks are always available, and a music room. The second floor consists of offices and meeting rooms of various sizes. The third floor contains several bedrooms used by the night hospital patients.

Dr. Glaser feels that the intimacy, friendliness, and warmth of the setting are important to this type of program. He feels that to be quartered in a hospital would pose a major environmental obstacle.

The staff

The entire day program staff consist of five professionals—the psychiatrist-director, two nurses, a vocational counselor, and a social worker—and two secretaries. Residents are assigned sporadically, for a two-month rotation.

During his residency Dr. Glaser was associated with Dr. Gardner at another university. After Dr. Gardner came to the Temple program, Dr. Glaser followed for the specific purpose of establishing a day program, even though he had had no exposure to such a program during his training or elsewhere.

In view of his decidedly "nonmedical orientation," as described below, we were curious to know why Dr. Glaser had chosen to use two nurses in such a small staff. "We were flying blind," he said. "We didn't know whether they would fit in, but we decided to see whether they would or not. Besides, we didn't particularly know what other kind of person we might try out. As it happened, we came up with two winners. I think their personal qualities have much more to do with their effectiveness than any training that they received. The training obviously adds a dimension of responsibility, but the most important thing is that their personal qualities enable them to deal with people in a very effective way." The social worker and the vocational counselor were highly experienced and seemed to be well trained.

"The most valuable training that any of us have had we received at Daytop Village, a narcotics treatment facility," said Dr. Glaser, "with a treatment program in Staten Island and a therapeutic community training program in the Catskills. All of us attended the training sessions while we were planning the program, and this had more influence on our operation than any other training of any kind. Indeed, our program is largely patterned after Daytop."

Staff meetings are held each morning for thirty minutes and on Friday afternoons for two hours. We attended a morning meeting at which the staff seemed to communicate very openly.

A resident who had recently completed his two-month rotation told us that he had found the program quite alien to any previous experience. He added that he had been impressed to see that in this program extremely sick patients quickly went into remission and showed remarkable improvement.

There has been limited use of volunteers. One who is from the Teacher Corps teaches two classes a week and conducts a puppet show which seeks to incorporate psychodrama techniques. "There is no reason why we could not use volunteers extensively," said Dr. Glaser. "Unfortunately, most who have approached us have done so through enthusiasm that was born of the moment and faded just as quickly. This may be because in this particular program one must put himself on the line as a person, which is often uncomfortable."

Referrals

We have mentioned that the day program is not an entry point; only in one case had a person been admitted "off the street." The total number of persons served during the first six months was probably not large enough to provide a reliable projection of where patients are likely to come from after the program is better established. By far the largest number had come from the Psychosocial Clinic, the next largest group from the Crisis Center. A few patients had been transferred to the day program from the Temple Unit at Philadelphia State Hospital, and a few others from the inpatient service at Temple University Hospital.

The program chose not to be a primary referral facility partly because experience in other day programs had indicated that unscreened referrals to day treatment programs were often inappropriate. "We are able to keep the staff of the psychiatry department and the community mental health center better informed about developments and policies in our partial hospitalization programs than we could the community at large," Dr. Glaser said. "Our staff are spared the time-consuming task of screening numerous applicants and making alternative dispositions when admission to the partial hospitalization programs is not indicated," he added. An obvious effect of this referral procedure is to limit admission to the kinds of patients each doctor thinks a day program should serve. ("But even so," Dr. Glaser added, "we get a wide variety of referrals because there is such disagreement among referral sources regarding who is appropriate. Furthermore, we are sometimes used as a 'dumping ground' for difficult cases whom no one else wants to handle. In any case it results in a membership that is problematic rather than placid.")

Even as a component of the community mental health center, this day program, like most others not doing its own intake, has had a hard time establishing a satisfactory flow of referrals. During its first few months it was necessary for the director to drum up business several times. After each reminder, the referring services would send a new spurt of patients for a brief time. This situation appeared to be the result of the customary reasons: the service was relatively new, the staff of the referring services had not been personally exposed to partial hospitalization programs.

Selection of patients

The referring services are asked not to refer persons who are actively suicidal or combative, who are stuporous, or who otherwise appear to require constant surveillance. Any other persons, provided they have an acceptable place to live, are accepted. In actuality, there had been no sex deviates other than homosexuals and no persons under the age of fourteen. There had been five narcotics addicts.

With its particularly strong emphasis on socialization, the program may well have a built-in selection factor, in that the socializable patient feels welcome and tends to stay, whereas the withdrawn patient or the patient who acts out and does not respond to group pressure may tend to be either weeded out or in some way excluded.

[Dr. Glaser commented in response to the manuscript, as follows:

I believe you are right that we have a selection factor, and I think you are not far wrong when you say that we select the socializable patient. However, lately we have come to somewhat different conclusions. We now think that perhaps the major goal of our program is to induce the people who come to us to surrender the "sick role" and its various attributes—exemption from responsibility, being entitled to special treatment, being permitted to have low expectations, expecting to be taken care of, and so forth. Even our group orientation can be seen as a part of this, since one could reason that the sick role includes the demand for special—i.e., individual, professional—attention. The sick role is obviously a hindrance to socialization, since obviously a person occupying this role cannot be fully socialized. Thus, our program may be conceptualized as being a transition from the unsocialized state of the sick role to the fully socialized state of belonging to the larger society.

In line with this, we have not been able to characterize our successes or failures along any of the standard diagnostic parameters. We succeed with some addicts, fail with others; succeed with some schizophrenics, fail with others; succeed with some alcoholics, fail with others. Obviously, what makes for success or failure is some trait that cuts across this nomenclature. We now feel that the trait is willingness to surrender the sickness role.

Apparently the sick role is quite independent of whether or not one is actually sick, if you wish to use that terminology. Most people would consider every schizophrenic sick. Yet, some adopt the sick role and some do not. It is a remarkable phenomenon; the role seems to be quite independent of anything else. We think we have seen cases in which people were not actually sick but were treated as such and adopted the sick role.]

A large number of persons exclude themselves, very early on. Like most of the other day programs we visited, the average length of stay is really described by a bimodal curve, with a large number of early dropouts. Dr. Glaser believes that the early dropouts are likely to be the sicker patients. It has been a particular problem to hold alcoholics in the program.

Characteristics of the patients

The patients gave every evidence of being severely ill.

Dr. Glaser maintains that most of them are not "social," and indeed have been far less social in the past than their behavior in the day program would suggest. "Many that you see here are in the process of becoming socialized," he said. "A good example is a woman who was purely autistic when she first came in, and with continued exposure to the program, she's not autistic anymore. Of course there are the others—they were autistic when they came in, and they still are. Some people we just can't get through to. Also, we find with many of them it isn't only a matter of too little socialization, but socialization of a very poor quality."

The people who stay in the program appear to be those who can tolerate various kinds of pressure, including that of talking and being talked about in the group and of being publicly called to account when they violate the rules.

About 40 percent are diagnosed as schizophrenic, about 20 percent as affective disorders, about 20 percent as personality disorders. The remaining 20 percent are scattered among various diagnoses. Almost half of the patients are men. The substantial majority are between 21 and 65 years old. There had been only one person over 65.

There have been a sufficient number of adolescents to lead to a separate adolescent group meeting, held weekly. The staff reserve to themselves the right to limit the number of adolescents, but had not found it necessary to do so.

On the day of our visit, there were eight men and thirteen women. All but three of these 21 persons were Negroes.

The average stay for those separated from the day program during early 1968 was fourteen days of attendance but this average includes a number of early dropouts. Dr. Glaser sees the ideal stay, once the program is better established, as two to three months and perhaps longer.

Treatment philosophy

By far the most interesting aspect of this program is the treatment philosophy of its staff. It would be interesting to know how many young psychiatrists share Dr. Glaser's concern about the traditional "medical model," which he describes as being exemplified by the "surgical emergency model" on the one hand and the psychoanalytic model on the other. What bothers him about both is the physician's role as omnipotent, and the distance between physician and patient. He has spelled out his convictions in a thoughtful and scholarly paper called "'Our Place': A Brief Summary of the Conceptual Background of the Day Program of the Temple University Community Mental Health Center." In a discussion of his understanding of the therapeutic community, Dr. Glaser says:

> To many, the democratic ideal implies equal influence of each upon each, that no man shall rise above his fellows. In practice, hierarchies

form within all human groups. Our feeling is that hierarchical structure is neither good nor bad in and of itself. It depends upon the basis of the structure. If its basis is professional rank, that is one thing; if it is what could be termed right action, that is another. That is, if the doctor is right, it is not because he is the doctor, but because he is right. His being a doctor may in some way enable him to be right, but then, being a patient may enable another person to be right. In most traditional, authoritarian medical settings, the doctor is right because he is the doctor. It is this that we seek to avoid.

(Dr. Glaser adds that it is not established that such a treatment philosophy produces superior results.)

The application of this philosophy to the structure of the day program is readily evident. Those who attend the program are *members* rather than *patients*. All staff persons and all members are on a mandatory first-name basis. Staff members are not allowed to display their certificates and diplomas. Although prescriptions are provided to the patients, no medications are dispensed on the premises.

Formal individual psychotherapy is absolutely prohibited, "in order to assure that the major business of the program is carried out in groups." All of the staff are classically trained, and Dr. Glaser fears that their greater comfort with individual treatment would subvert the groups, turning them into mere formalities. There is no objection, however, to a given member's continuing in individual psychotherapy with a therapist outside the day program, although there were no such patients until the program had been operating for some months. It is important to realize, too, that a great deal of informal one-to-one contact takes place, and is encouraged.

"Our final goal," Dr. Glaser states, "is to unlock the human potential that we feel is all too often stifled by the professional role and to promote person-to-person engagement. One reason that this may not have been more widely attempted in the past is that it is personally far less comfortable."

The treatment program

A therapeutic community. The therapeutic community appeared to be a very fine one, particularly so in view of its relative newness. Said one of the consultants, "Unlike many programs that call themselves therapeutic communities and build in activity programs of questionable relevance, the members in this therapeutic community are given the task of building and maintaining the social community. All activities are related to this task."

Each patient is assigned to one of four committees: a membership committee responsible for making home visits, contacting patients who fail to attend, and other membership matters; a kitchen committee responsible for ordering and carting meals from the main hospital and preparing meals for special occasions; a maintenance committee responsible for the physical setting of the house, including obtaining furnishings and equipment; and a social committee that plans and arranges various activities and outings.

Each member belongs, additionally, to one of three "house groups," which are therapy groups that meet twice a week. "We have tried hard to make these 'leaderless' groups," said Dr. Glaser. "We think the group members are less dependent on the professional than groups we know of in other programs. We like to think that the professional is present as much to record information for the charts as for anything else."

The entire membership attends a community meeting for thirty minutes each morning. This meeting, led by one of the patients, is used to discuss community problems and to refer them for solution as indicated to one of the four committees described above.

We attended one of the community meetings, at which 21 patients and six staff members were present. With one or two exceptions, the patients appeared to be moderately to enthusiastically involved. There seemed to be proportionately greater participation by the staff, who used the meeting to pass on information of an administrative nature, such as a request for better housekeeping liaison with the night hospital program, and also to inform the members about other members who had had significant events in their lives outside of the day program. From the members there were occasional humorously couched expressions of hostility toward the staff, which were deliberately not responded to. On the whole, it appeared to be an extraordinarily open meeting, in which the staff were unaffected and did everything they could to reduce the distance between themselves and the patients. The patients seemed quite comfortable in relating socially to the staff.

All members and staff are expected to attend two types of evaluation conferences, and most do so. One of these is the *initial evaluation,* which takes place after a member has been in the group for two weeks. The new member's problems are discussed, and his entire chart is read. The frequency of his attendance is determined, and he is assigned to a committee and a therapy group. We attended such a session, at which a woman patient was interviewed essentially by the staff. Considerable pressure was exerted to encourage her involvement. It appeared that this meeting, in addition to carrying out its designated business, served a concurrent therapeutic purpose—as a training session not only for the member being evaluated but for all of the group members, in terms of understanding the dynamics of emotional disturbances, expressing and exploring feelings, and developing the concept of reciprocal responsibility and concern.

The second type of evaluation meeting is the *ongoing evaluation,* scheduled three times a week to review the progress of longer-involved patients. These sessions take place for a given patient at intervals of four to six weeks.

An interesting device for managing uncooperative members is a group confrontation called "the haircut." Any staff person and any of the senior members may declare such a confrontation in the face of any infraction of rules, and this then takes priority over all other activities.

The enthusiasm and high morale of the staff make the program an exciting one to witness. Dr. Glaser's conscientious efforts to flatten the status hierarchy and to delegate maximum responsibility to his staff have clearly achieved a degree of success. The major problem of the program appeared to be the attempt to impose a foreign culture, specifically a therapeutic community, on a group of extremely deprived people of a cultural background entirely different from that of the staff. This imposed culture, with its concepts of democratization, permissiveness, interdependency, free expression of feeling, and psychosocial etiology of somatic and behavioral disorders must seem quite confusing to new members; it certainly appears to be contrary to their own past experiences and to reality as they perceive it in the urban slum. Dr. Glaser comments: "I agree that the therapeutic community differs from the deprived community, but I think it differs at least as much from the affluent community, and certainly it differs from the medical and psychiatric communities."

We suspected that the program could reduce its dropout rate if it were to provide more extensive orientation, and if the initial evaluation sessions took place after two or three days rather than after two weeks. (Since the time of our visit an "orientation group" has been added, which meets with the new member on his first day and "shepherds" him through the day. This has lowered the early dropout rate.)

Activities. Much of the day is used up in the various group meetings described above. There are also various special groups, including a women's group led by one of the nurses, an adolescents group, an analytically oriented group which had been started shortly before our visit, and a couples group. There is also a weekly psychodrama session, and an "instructional group" with educational, as contrasted with therapeutic, intent. Approximately an hour a day of free time is allowed. There is no occupational therapy in the usual sense, but rather projects needed to facilitate the operation of the community. For example, some members were renovating old sewing machines so that they might be used by women members who wanted to improve their sewing skills. Apart from a weekly two-hour session at a nearby gymnasium, there are no formal recreational activities. The patients engage in occasional group projects, such as preparing dinner for the mental health center staff in order to earn money to pay for field trips, and in occasional special activities such as planting the back yard and renovating the basement.

Said Dr. Glaser, "We are beginning to think it was a blessing that we had very limited operating funds. This situation made us work, and it placed us in the mainstream of social events. We're now considering opening a small business, perhaps a coffee shop or a restaurant."

Medication. Between half and two thirds of patients regularly take psychotropic drugs. Dr. Glaser holds a "prescription hour" weekly, but it is each member's responsibility to get his prescription filled. Many are covered for drugs by the welfare department, and others can get their prescriptions filled at a reduced rate at the Temple University dispensary.

Dr. Glaser believes it is important to make the members responsible for their own medication. "You do people a disservice when you abrogate their independent function," he said. "We felt that to have our staff defined as nurses who urge pills on members was inimical to our goal, and so we handle the medications pretty much as an outpatient clinic would do. Unless you hospitalize a person indefinitely, you'll never be able to push medication on him. Frequently we've been able to say to one of our members, 'Look, you're acting crazy and we can't understand what you're saying, and you can't participate effectively in the groups unless we can understand you, so why don't you take your medicine?' And it works."

Home visits. At least one home visit is made to each patient, not only by staff members but by fellow patients as well. This interesting twist came about fortuitously. A psychiatric resident who was frightened by the prospect of making a home visit alone arranged to accompany one of the staff members. Still apprehensive afterward, he decided spontaneously to take some of the patients with him; this particular visit worked out so well that it became a regular procedure to include the patients.

Dr. Glaser relates the story of a paranoid patient who asked, "What is this home-visiting business? Do you mean you actually go into people's homes? I don't understand it." He told her that the best way to understand would be for her to come with him when he visited someone. "She came with me and handled the whole visit—beautifully. Then when we went to her home, it turned out beautifully. She felt better and it cut down on her suspicions."

Boarding. There is no provision for boarding a day patient overnight. Even if beds are available on the night program, day patients are not held over there except in the most unusual circumstances.

Work-for-pay. There are no organized group work activities. Individual patients sometimes arrange to do work while they are at the house. At the time of our visit one woman was doing ironing for pay for staff members and her fellow patients, and another was making potholders to sell.

Rehabilitation. The most important goal of this program can be stated as getting people back into a useful central life role, which for all of the men and many of the women is work. A number of the members have been placed in jobs. Among this very small staff, one member is a full-time vocational counselor. She attends all evaluations. There is regularly scheduled vocational group testing plus a weekly vocational group discussion. Plans were being made for a bimonthly "employment review," a full-member session at which the employment status of every individual would be reviewed.

Through a separate component of the mental health center, there are opportunities for day program members to participate in a private sheltered workshop and to apply for the state's vocational rehabilitation services.

Disposition. Twelve persons were separated from the day program during the first two months of 1968. Seven of these were released without provision for further treatment; two were transferred to Philadelphia State Hospital; one was transferred to inpatient status at Temple University Hospital; and two were transferred to outpatient status. Discharged patients are welcome to return as visitors.

Outcome. The program is too recently established to have any data on outcome of treatment. A cohort study was being planned.

Records

Complete records are kept for all members. Those who transfer from other components of the mental health center have their records transferred. A note is written at least once a week by the leader of the member's therapy group. Notes are made of the initial and ongoing evaluations, and notes for special groups are written as indicated. All notes are written with the assumption that the member is likely to hear them.

Transportation

The facility is located a short distance from Broad Street, which is one of the city's principal transportation axes. Most of the patients live within walking distance or else use one of the Broad Street bus lines. For those who live in the more remote parts of the catchment area, transportation is a major problem. The welfare department readily provides bus fare, and for one pregnant woman it paid taxi fare.

Agency relationships

We were told that the full-time social worker maintains a regular and effective relationship with a variety of agencies whose services might be needed by the day program members, including, notably, welfare, the housing authority, and legal aid.

Placements

There is one boardinghouse in the neighborhood to which an occasional patient needing a place to live has been referred. Described as warm and homelike, it is run by a woman who worked for some years as an aide in a mental hospital. Dr. Glaser expressed the view that programs such as his could handle a considerably larger share of the mentally disordered if there were more boardinghouses of this kind available. He said that by contrast there were in Philadelphia various boardinghouses that accept mental patients in which the facilities and amenities are not nearly as good as those of the mental hospitals from which the patients come.

Financing

The community mental health center as a whole was still in the process of developing a fee schedule, and various adjustments had already been made. A theoretical charge of $20 per day is made in the day program, but in fact none of the patients pay anything at all, except for occasional ones who have health insurance or some form of public third-party payment. At present the costs of the program are being met by a combination of federal and state funds.

Subsequent to our visit a new fee schedule was worked out. Identical to the outpatient fee, it is based on income and size of family. An interesting aspect is that it is set for a weekly period, irrespective of the number of visits. Thus, patients needing more frequent contact are not financially penalized.

Plans for the future

Apart from building up a reliable referral procedure that will enable it to maintain a daily census of about thirty, this day program does not plan to expand. There will be some added emphasis upon sinking roots in the community, but essentially the same type of client will be served, with the same goals as at present.

The director of this program and the director of the entire center agreed that additional day hospitals might be desirable, both in terms of their being situated in community satellites now being planned by the center, and in terms of serving other purposes. However, these additional units probably will not be established, since funds cannot be obtained to acquire and remodel the physical structures they would require.

There were plans to add two additional staff members, one of them a former patient of the day program who had been trained in the center's mental health assistant program. The other new employee was to be an "indigenous nonprofessional."

Longer-term plans for the center are likely to have a great effect on the day program. Specifically, in mid-1968 the decision was taken to phase out the inpatient service at Philadelphia State Hospital, because of a growing concern that too many patients were being hospitalized simply because of the availability of beds. Thus, it may be that additional day programs will be required, along with a home treatment service and a greater number of supervised residential placements.

Veterans Administration Hospital
Minneapolis

THE DAY HOSPITAL at the Minneapolis Veterans Administration Hospital was the first to be established in the Veterans Administration system. In 1961 the chief of psychiatry at Minneapolis Veterans Administration Hospital, Dr. Werner Simon, requested authority and funds to establish a day hospital. He proposed that day hospitals should be attached to general hospitals, where all diagnostic and treatment facilities would be readily available. The day hospital, he said, would eliminate the costly "hotel function" for "the patient who needs services found *at* a hospital but who does not need to stay *in* a hospital." He hypothesized that the day hospital would increase the utilization of inpatient facilities, and that it could substitute for and supplement hospitalization for those with major psychosis, serious psychoneurosis, and involutional or senile states considered too severe for outpatient treatment or not eligible for outpatient service.

Following complicated deliberations within the Veterans Administration concerning the legality of an intensity of treatment intermediate between outpatient care and total hospitalization, Dr. Simon received approval in July 1965 to undertake a pilot program.

The Central Office of the Veterans Administration appears, under the direction of Dr. John Blasko, who was Director of the Psychiatry, Neurology, and Psychology Service until his death in mid-1968, to have endorsed and emphasized day treatment as accomplishing the goals and purposes that Dr. Simon put forth.

Physical plant

The day hospital is located on an upper floor of the main building of the Veterans Administration Hospital complex, located toward one edge of the city of Minneapolis. For some years this building has contained a 102-bed inpatient psychiatric service. The day hospital did not require any new facilities other than office space for its small staff. The predischarge ward dayroom, with kitchen facilities, was designated

118

for daytime use by the day hospital; it continues to be used after 5 p.m. each day and on weekends for its original purpose. Day patients and day hospital staff make use at stipulated times of the same lounge, group therapy and conference rooms, occupational therapy shop, manual arts shop, and various recreational facilities that serve the inpatients.

The setting is pleasant and comfortable along institutional lines. The amount of space appears to be adequate.

Capacity and range of census

The stated capacity of the day hospital is 30. The range during 1967 was from 11 to 32. During a week in mid-January 1968, there were 25 persons who attended.

The staff

The psychiatrist-director, Dr. Edward Posey, completed his residency at Minneapolis Veterans Administration Hospital in 1965 and stayed on to start the day hospital. He has administrative responsibility for the entire day program, clinical responsibility for certain patients, and additionally is the physician for a few patients on the inpatient service, particularly those who have been transferred there from the day hospital.

There is a full-time psychiatric resident, assigned on the basis of a six-month elective. The only other full-time staff members are a social worker and a registered nurse. There is a half-time psychologist, a half-time industrial therapist, a three-quarter-time occupational therapist, and a few hours of service each week from a manual arts therapist and an alcoholism counselor.

"The day hospital staff interact more closely and with greater flexibility and versatility of role functioning than most traditional clinical teams," Dr. Simon said. "In addition to formal weekly team meetings, informal meetings are held throughout the day with staff or patients whenever indicated, in accordance with the concept of the 'free floating' therapist who interacts with patients in all types of situations. In this regard, all members of the day hospital staff, in addition to their basic specialized functions, share the responsibility of creating and maintaining a therapeutic milieu. The various activities provide many therapeutic opportunities by applying techniques such as support, interpretation, direction and guidance, catharsis, environmental manipulation, desensitization, behavior modification, and relearning. Staff members write progress notes on their patients on one consolidated form, which is shared by all.

All of the staff attend 'multiple impact' interviews of patients, at which time definite goals for day hospital treatment for the particular patient are agreed upon. Regardless of their primary discipline, staff members take turns as leaders in group psychotherapy and sociodrama. All of this allows for a high degree of originality and flexibility, and requires maturity in direction and security in role functioning."

We interviewed all of the full-time and most of the part-time staff members and were impressed with their evident skill and enthusiasm.

Referrals

Most of the patients who enter the day hospital come from one of two sources: on transfer from the inpatient service or directly through the admitting psychiatrist for the psychiatry service. (The occasional exceptions are persons who have been referred by private sources with a specific recommendation for day hospital treatment; these are processed through the admitting psychiatrist.)

During the first year of operation 36 percent of admissions were direct and 64 percent were transfers from the inpatient service. During the second year the direct admissions increased dramatically, to 59 percent. There appear to have been several reasons. One was the increased use of the day hospital to hold seriously sick patients for whom no inpatient bed was available. In such cases the day hospital was seen as an alternative preferable to sending the patient to the nearest Veterans Administration neuropsychiatric hospital, located some seventy miles from Minneapolis. A second was the emergence of a group of patients for whom the day program appeared to be the treatment intensity of choice; many of these were not sick enough to warrant inpatient service but were too disturbed to be handled by the separate Veterans Administration outpatient clinic.

There has been a problem from the outset concerning referrals from the inpatient service. Some of this is attributed to the lack of familiarity both of the psychiatric residents and the senior staff, all of whom carry patients, with day hospital treatment, and some of it is ascribed to the reluctance of the residents to give up patients with whom they have only recently become involved. The principal problem is probably the former, since it has been explicit from the outset that residents on the inpatient service are free to continue to follow patients that they transfer to the day hospital. It is also possibly significant that the day hospital staff reserve to themselves the privilege of passing on the suitability of each inpatient suggested for transfer to the day hospital; although no such patient has ever been refused, the mere existence of this formal acceptance procedure may impede referrals.

Dr. Simon described the efforts to set up adequate channels of referral: "I talked with members of the Minnesota Psychiatric Society, and I also gave some talks here at the hospital. But we worked primarily through individuals. When the inpatient service was full, I would say to our psychiatrists, 'Look, some of your patients here don't need 24-hour care any longer. They go on weekend passes regularly. If you'll refer them to the day hospital, we'll help you with individual decisions.' This brought us some patients. We went to the hospital's general admission office, where the social worker plays an important role. We acquainted the social workers in the medical services with our day hospital program and invited them to refer medical patients needing psychiatric treatment. But most of all, we worked with our admitting psychiatrist, Dr. Margaret Bailey, who before long began to screen the patients who could be suitably placed on day treatment."

Selection procedure

For a veteran applying for psychiatric treatment, Dr. Bailey has at her disposal *a*) the inpatient service, provided a bed is available, *b*) the day hospital, *c*) referral to the separately operated Veterans Administration outpatient clinic, and *d*) referral to the Veterans Administration neuropsychiatric hospital at St. Cloud, Minnesota. She described the criteria for placing a patient on day status as follows:

• He must live close enough to be able to commute. (He is asked to provide his own transportation, but in case he cannot, the social service department often obtains funds for him.)

• He must have an acceptable place to live, preferably with relatives who are sympathetic and supportive but in any case a "home base where he can get along at least in a borderline fashion at night and on weekends."

• He must not be suicidal or homicidal or otherwise pose a major management problem.

Dr. Bailey indicated day hospital works well for patients with a wide range of psychiatric difficulties. Examples are the depressed person who is dependent and requires temporary psychological support, the person experiencing an anxiety reaction or who is in a panic state but doesn't need to be in the hospital, immature individuals who display some features of a character disorder but who are young enough to respond to treatment, ambulatory psychotic patients who are beginning to decompensate and require the temporary support of day hospitalization to interrupt this process, and retired people who are undergoing situational depressions and need help in developing interests, hobbies, or even in doing part-time work or volunteer service for the hospital. Alcoholics may also be treated if they are sober on admission and appear able to remain sober with the support of the day hospital, including participation in the special alcohol treatment program within the day hospital.

Characteristics of the patients

Of 190 persons who were patients in the day hospital during 1967, only one was under 21 and only one was over 65. All except three were men.

The modal diagnosis was psychoneurotic disorder, accounting for slightly more than half of all admissions (52 percent). Next came alcoholism with 23 percent; schizophrenic reaction, 12 percent; personality disorder, seven percent; and all others combined, seven percent.

We were told that a great many of the day hospital patients have had little or no previous hospitalization. "They come to us in an acute stage," said the psychiatric resident, "usually in crisis. We do have some chronically inadequate patients, but many of our patients, including the schizophrenics, are fairly middle class. Our depressed patients are particularly middle class—accountants and federal employees. By and large these men are quite different from the patients I saw at a state hospital where I worked before coming here."

The job placement office told us that many of the day patients had been working shortly or immediately prior to hospitalization. "The length of time since they were working is often only a few days and rarely more than a month," he said, "but the loss of a job in many cases contributed to their problems and precipitated their admission."

A moderate number of the day patients live alone. At the time of our visit there were six alcoholic patients, either bachelors or divorcees, who were living alone; two others who had no permanent residence when they came to the program had been placed in rooming houses by the social worker.

We asked Dr. Bailey where she would have placed the day hospital patients if there had been no day hospital. "Some of them I would have admitted to the inpatient service," she said. "A number of them I would have referred to some kind of outpatient help at another facility."

Treatment philosophy

"The day hospital affords the patient an opportunity to gain a 'derivative insight,' " said Dr. Posey. "By this we mean that the symptoms of his illness are recognized as abnormalities or morbid phenomena. The insight is arrived at by the patient himself, without interpretation by the therapist, in a manner generally characteristic of activity therapy groups. This phenomenon usually takes place within the first two weeks of hospitalization, but if it should occur very early, we suspect that the patient is making a flight into health, denial, or a deliberate attempt to 'cover up' his problems, in which case the staff encourage him to remain in treatment longer.

"If he persists in his desire to leave the program, we feel that he is not motivated at the present time to work on the problems that caused him to seek psychiatric help. This transference-resistance is immediately dealt with. The staff nurse attempts to contact the patient on the following day, at which time he is encouraged to reconsider and to arrange for a longer interview with the social worker. Rarely do we have this resistance problem with the schizophrenic. We think the schizophrenic remains because of the combination of the staff's motivation to help him, the patient's idea that he has been selected for a special group that requires only partial hospitalization, and a warm but non-threatening approach to the patient. The basic trust expounded by Frieda Fromm-Reichmann in *The Principles of Intensive Psychotherapy* is felt to be quite necessary. Through this approach, a reorganization of the fragmented ego is more quickly accomplished, as evidenced by the patient's willingness to deal with reality, his improvement in appearance and behavior, and his feeling that he is no longer different from the majority of people in the world where he lives."

Dr. Simon feels that despite the heavy demand at all times for inpatient beds, his program could furnish adequate service with the present 102 beds, provided the means could be found to expand the day hospital program substantially. "I'd venture that we can perform as well with a 100-bed inpatient unit and a large day hospital as we could with a 350-bed inpatient unit and no day hospital," he said. "If we had the staff available it would be quite possible to expand the day hospital to a capacity of 150."

Several members of the staff, when asked to characterize the treatment program in terms of directiveness vs. permissiveness, said they see it as more directive than the average program. For example, group leaders are appointed rather than elected, an approach which one staff member attributed more to tradition than to any conviction on the part of the administration. The resident characterized the treatment philosophy as "confrontation and clarification." Said another staff member, "We focus more on current living situations; we don't dig into the psyche. We expect the patients to carry out the assignments made to them, and on their part there's none of the feeling that 'I can't do it' or 'Someone has to help me.' They're expected to pull their own weight from the very beginning."

The treatment program

This day hospital has developed a very broad range of treatment modalities, including medication, individual contacts, group activities, job training, job placement, and so on. This appeared to have resulted from an awareness that since the efficacy of individual modalities for given types of patients is not yet well established, it seems suitable to provide the broadest possible program in the hope that various individuals will find within it something that will serve to ameliorate their particular impairment.

The day hospital is open from 8:30 a.m. to 5:00 p.m. on Monday through Friday. Initially patients are expected to come five days a week. When an individual appears to have improved and to be able to take on more responsibility for independent living, his schedule is reduced, usually to two or three days per week. For patients released from day status during 1967, the "stay" came to 21 treatment days, or, in a typical case, three weeks at a frequency of five days per week, followed by three weeks at a frequency of two days per week.

Patient-staff relationships. Each patient is first evaluated by the day hospital director, and then, on the subsequent Tuesday or Thursday, he is seen by the entire staff at an admission conference. "We attempt at this conference to make it clear what we can do to help him," said a member of the staff, "but we also make it clear that we expect him to put forth some effort, too, that he will be required to participate, that this is not like a medical service where things are simply done to him."

A member of the staff is designated coordinator for each patient, in an arrangement that seems quite like the "primary therapist" role of the staff at Syracuse Psychiatric Hospital. This provides the patient a confidant that he can turn to with his day-to-day problems. The coordinator helps the patient to deal with his problem if it seems suitable; otherwise, he refers him to a more appropriate member of the staff. The contacts with the coordinator are not considered to be psychotherapy in the conventional sense. A number of patients are seen, however, in formal, scheduled individual psychotherapy, which for the most part is characterized as supportive rather than dynamic.

Most of the patients are seen in group therapy, scheduled twice weekly, consisting of small, open-ended groups led by the psychiatrist, the resident, the psychologist, or the social worker.

Medication. About ninety percent of the patients are on psychotropic medications. "We don't use drugs as routinely, however, as most inpatient services do," we were told. "There seems on the inpatient service to be some need to justify *not giving* medication, whereas here we are more inclined to feel that we have to justify *giving* medication." Drugs are furnished free; the day patients call at the hospital pharmacy on a designated afternoon each week to obtain a one-week supply.

The schedule. The day begins with a 45-minute community meeting, followed by a two-hour industrial therapy assignment. Soon after admission each patient is interviewed by the industrial therapist (who is also the job placement officer) and then assigned to a job in the hospital. "Performance on an industrial therapy assignment helps us understand and assist you with possible employment problems you may be experiencing," a handbook for day patients explains.

There is a weekly occupational therapy session of the traditional kind, involving art, ceramics, leatherwork, weaving, etc. There are two manual arts therapy sessions per week, taking place in a well-equipped woodworking and metal workshop. There is a weekly group recreational activity, such as bowling, golf, or a field trip. Every Friday afternoon the recreation department provides refreshments and holds a songfest in the day hospital dayroom.

Work-for-pay. There is no work-for-pay program in the day hospital. However, the industrial therapist has arranged for a local factory to employ certain day hospital patients on a regularly scheduled competitive but trial basis.

Boarding. It is rarely necessary to board an agitated day patient in the inpatient service. However, in the face of prolonged management problems it sometimes becomes necessary to transfer day patients to formal inpatient status.

Family involvement. The social worker arranges an interview with the patient and his relatives shortly after the patient begins the day hospital program. If relatives accompany the patient during admission, they are seen at that time. The day hospital is described to the family, treatment goals are clarified, and continued communication with the day hospital staff is encouraged. Family members are frequently also involved in additional treatment interviews.

Disposition and outcome. During 1967 there were 159 patients released from the day hospital, to the following dispositions:

To full employment	60%
To inpatient status at Minneapolis VA Hospital	14
To private physicians for further care	9
To VA training and education programs	6
To provide volunteer service within Minneapolis VA Hospital	3
To inpatient service other than Minneapolis VA Hospital	3
To outpatient status, VA clinic	2
To workhouse, probation	2
Without provision for further treatment	1

Even in view of the fact that the modal diagnosis in this day hospital is psychoneurotic disorder, it is quite impressive that during 1967 three out of every five patients left the program to return to full employment.

Partial figures for fiscal 1968 indicate a still higher rate of discharge to full employment—133 of 177 patients, or 75 percent. Of these, 101 returned to their previous jobs and 32 found new jobs. This reflects in part the fact that many of the patients are less disorganized and decompensated than those of the inpatient service, but it also reflects the strong emphasis on rehabilitation to work, plus the specific efforts made to induce employers to allow the patients to return to their jobs following hospitalization.

As for the fourteen percent rate of transfer to the inpatient service, it should be remembered that the day hospital is sometimes used as a holding operation for persons who, if a bed were available, would have been assigned directly to the inpatient service. (Included in these transfers are persons who become inpatients for medical-surgical reasons.) In these circumstances, the rate of transfer seems a moderate one.

Transportation

The hospital is moderately accessible by public transportation for persons living in the Minneapolis-St. Paul area. A minority of patients do not have bus fare available, in which case the social worker obtains it for them from a small "emergency fund." There has been an occasional problem with an applicant for day hospital care who lives at great distance but insists that he can commute. "Some people would be willing to spend two hours each way on the bus," said Dr. Posey, "but we consider that excessive. We usually draw the line at one hour commuting time."

Agency relationships

The social worker deals actively with agencies that provide family counseling, recreation, and financial assistance. For patients unable to work but needing something to do with their time, she arranges placements in agencies that use volunteer workers. She also frequently locates rooming houses and boarding homes for single patients who do not have a suitable place to live.

The job placement officer maintains frequent contacts with employers of patients and also seeks out jobs for unemployed patients.

Financing

The cost of this program, including lunch, is met entirely by the federal government, and consequently there is no financial deterrent to the patients' making full use of the program. In this light the rather short average attendance of 21 days is of particular interest.

Figures for early 1968 indicate that the cost per visit in the day hospital was $25.40, contrasted with $38.60 for the inpatient service. Since the average attendance for day patients is between three and four days per week, this brings the weekly cost to the vicinity of $75 to $100 per week, contrasted with a weekly inpatient cost of approximately $270.

Future plans

This hospital's psychiatric service feels that the success of its day hospital program is readily apparent—indeed, to such an extent that the staff would like to see day hospitalization greatly expanded and inpatient capacity held at its present level. Whether this will be possible, either in this hospital or elsewhere in the Veterans Administration network, will depend in large part on the future course of the Veterans Administration Central Office in Washington. Considering the substantial increase in partial hospitalization services within the Veterans Administration overall, there is good reason to hope that this hospital and its counterparts, which comprise the world's largest medical system, will be a major, and perhaps the most important, factor in helping this country to realize the potential of partial hospitalization for the psychiatric patient.

Prairie View Mental Health Center
Newton, Kansas

PRAIRIE VIEW Mental Health Center is a small, high-quality mental health facility located in a small town about 25 miles from Wichita, Kansas. It developed from a private psychiatric hospital founded by the Mennonite Mental Health Services in 1954. During the hospital's early years, when it was staffed on a contractual basis by psychiatrists from Wichita, it provided primarily inpatient treatment. In 1961, when it began to operate with its own staff, Prairie View began to broaden its program. In 1963, under the Kansas Community Mental Health Services Act, the hospital contracted to provide outpatient and consultation services on a fee-for-service basis, to the county in which it is located and later to two adjacent counties, with a combined population of 65,000. Since 1964, with the aid of a National Institute of Mental Health demonstration grant, it has furnished aftercare service to all former state hospital patients returning to their homes in this three-county area. It was one of the first programs in the country to apply for a federal community mental health center construction grant. Since 1966 it has been a fully operational community mental health center within the context of the federal program.

The partial hospitalization service is largely limited to a day hospital. Initially day hospitalization took place informally, as an overlay on the inpatient service. In 1964 a small separate day hospital program was instituted. In 1967 the day hospital moved to its own building. The program as it existed in 1968 is of interest in terms of a) the evidence that day care is a feasible means of treatment for certain patients in a sparsely settled area, b) the use of day care as an evaluative-diagnostic medium, and c) the extent to which restrictions and limitations of health insurance and public funds can hamstring a program that attempts to provide a comprehensive range of treatment and can greatly affect the patterns of treatment.

128

Physical plant

Prairie View Mental Health Center consists of an attractively laid-out complex of five single-story buildings, all of which are spacious and pleasant; the newer ones are among the most attractive that we have seen in any mental health facility. The day hospital occupies its own large and separate building, flanked on one side by an activities building and on the other by the industrial therapy shop. The separate building seems to give the program special identity. There is a large combination lobby and lounge with recreation space, a group room, a quiet room with a day bed, and office space for the staff. All of the rooms are large, open, and cheerful. The facilities would be commodious for an average attendance of thirty or more patients.

Capacity and range of census

The stated capacity of the day hospital is twenty per day. During 1967 the daily census ranged from three to seventeen. During the course of a week in January 1968 thirty different patients attended.

The staff

Prairie View has a staff equivalent to 78 full-time persons, of whom the equivalent of approximately three full-time positions are assigned to the day hospital. The only full-time person is a registered nurse, who has worked with the day hospital as long as it has operated as a separate entity. He is both coordinator for the day patients and administrator for the day program.

There are two aides, each spending approximately half time in the day hospital. A social worker spends five hours per week in the program, specifically as therapist for a daily group therapy session at which the nurse serves as co-therapist. Since day patients may spend their afternoons away from the day hospital building, engaging in various activities, a certain portion of the time of activity therapists is therefore devoted to day patients. Because of the use of "add on" therapies there is less emphasis on therapeutic community than at some of the other programs we visited.

At the time of our visit psychiatric involvement in the day program was limited to about four hours per week, consisting of a brief daily round to discuss specific medication and management problems, plus a weekly meeting to review the status of day patients. Earlier, when there was a third psychiatrist on the Prairie View staff, psychiatric time for the day program had been about seven hours a week; a replacement for this psychiatrist was scheduled to come in mid-1968, and it was anticipated that additional psychiatric time would then become available.

Only one volunteer had been used in the program. She came from a distant town to provide transportation for some of the patients living near her and incidentally to assist in the crafts program. As these patients left the program and as the volunteer became involved with other responsibilities, she tapered her time off and then stopped. Active plans were under way to develop a volunteer program for the center as a whole, including the day program.

Referrals

Almost three fifths of the day patients come from within the hospital. Specifically, 46 percent are transferred from the inpatient service, and for them the day program serves as a transitional arrangement as they become more independent, responsible, and autonomous. An additional eleven percent are transferred from the outpatient service; by and large they are persons who began as outpatients and then appeared to need more intensive care.

The remaining 43 percent are assigned directly to the day program by one of the hospital's two examining psychiatrists. Among patients admitted directly to the day hospital during 1967, the sources of referral to Prairie View were as follows:

Welfare department	26%
Self	26
Relatives	19
Family physicians	12
Aftercare, from state hospital	10
Friends	5
Ministers	2

Selection procedure

The day hospital is not used as a treatment setting for persons who are a) severely depressed, b) acting out, c) court-committed, d) actively alcoholic, e) actively suicidal or homicidal. More than three quarters of the patients are adults, although Prairie View's medical director, Dr. Mitchell Jones, told us that it could well include more adolescents.

A frequent and necessary exclusion from the day hospital program of this private nonprofit center results from the patient's inability to pay or to qualify for treatment under the regulations of the three counties which Prairie View serves (as described below under "financing").

Characteristics of the patients

Among 104 persons who were on day status during 1967, just under two thirds (64 percent) were women.

Exactly three quarters were between 21 and 65 years old, 18 percent were under 21, and seven percent were over 65.

The modal diagnosis was psychoneurotic disorder, accounting for 37 percent. Other diagnoses were as follows:

Schizophrenic reaction	22%
Personality disorder	18
Depressive psychotic reaction	7
Chronic brain syndrome	5
Stress and adjustment reaction	5
Alcoholism	4
Manic-depressive reaction	3

All of the staff persons we interviewed were inclined to feel that most of the direct admissions to the day hospital were less severely ill than most of the inpatients, indicating that the day hospital is not viewed as an alternative to 24-hour care for the severely disturbed patient. However, compared to the other facilities we visited, a relatively high percentage of day patients are transferred to the inpatient service —seventeen percent during 1967. This reflects the fact that the day hospital is often resorted to as a "holding operation" when no beds are available. Sometimes the patients thus placed do respond to the day hospital program, but a number of them require transfer to inpatient status when a bed becomes available. Somewhat incidentally, this situation brought about a realization that the day hospital can be a useful diagnostic and evaluative procedure. As contrasted with the more typical procedure whereby an examining physician (or in some programs, a nonphysician) determines on the basis of a brief interview whether a patient requires inpatient, outpatient, or some other intensity of treatment, the temporary placement in the day hospital allows a fairly intensive exposure of the patient to a variety of professionals. This procedure might be worth adoption by other programs even if only an occasional person who would otherwise be considered to require inpatient care should turn out to respond to day treatment.

By social and economic background, the vast majority of patients are middle class. However, there is a complete range within the program. There are a few well-to-do patients who pay for treatment from their own resources, while a substantial number of other patients would be unable to afford the fees were it not for health insurance, welfare, and county mental health funds.

Treatment philosophy

Said Dr. Jones: "We feel that the core of our therapeutic effort is that we provide a setting in which: a) people can look at themselves in action, b) they can learn new social, work, and recreation skills, c) they can try out new kinds of behavior, and d) they can mobilize energy and motivation for change."

The day patients and day program staff are seen as constituting a simple community social structure in which a variety of activities are available. "Hopefully," Dr. Jones said, "a sense of mutual acceptance exists within this community so that honest expression and honest feedback are possible both in group and in individual exchanges."

The patient is seen as having "partnership responsibility" with the staff in using the treatment program to bring about changes in himself. Individual treatment goals for patients are set by patients and staff together. These goals may include not only relief from symptoms but also may aim at changing the patient's way of looking at himself and of dealing with the world.

The treatment program

Day patients are expected to arrive by nine o'clock but may come as early as eight. Those who arrive early have an informal coffee hour. At nine o'clock there is a planning meeting that lasts only as long as it is necessary for the patients and the nurse to decide what to do that morning, or in some cases to make advance plans for an outing. The morning may then be spent in outdoor recreation, table games, bowling, a field trip, or some group activity within the day hospital building. At 10:45, if there is a new patient or if it is otherwise indicated, there is a fifteen-minute visit from one of the psychiatrists for which no additional fee is charged. At eleven o'clock all of the day patients participate in group therapy on the unit, led by the social worker and the nurse. Day patients then have their lunch in the hospital dining room.

Some of the day patients, for financial reasons, stay only during the morning (see below). Those who spend the entire day meet briefly after lunch to discuss the afternoon schedule and then all of them deploy to industrial therapy, arts and crafts, the general shop, the activity center, psychodrama, or individual therapy sessions.

Approximately half of the day patients are in individual therapy, with psychiatrist, psychologist, or social worker, for which there is an additional charge. These appointments take place at the outpatient building, where the therapists' offices are located. There are usually three or four day patients who participate in the weekly psychodrama sessions. On a given afternoon there are likely to be a few day patients each in the various activities.

Medication. Approximately seventy percent of day patients receive psychotropic medications. Prescriptions are provided, and each patient is responsible for obtaining his own supply of drugs.

Work-for-pay. Prairie View has had an impressive work-for-pay program for about five years, with contracts and subcontracts from local industries. Tractor seats and golf-cart seats have been principal products. Inpatients, outpatients, and day patients all participate in this work-for-pay program (called, at this hospital, industrial therapy, a term which most state hospitals use to denote doing the hospital's work, usually without compensation).

Patients must be able to meet the production requirements of the industrial therapy shop, since it is required to earn its own way. Some patients are paid an hourly rate identical to the federal minimum wage, while others are paid on a piecework basis. Surprisingly, the piecework arrangement is not used for those too slow to qualify for the hourly wage, but instead is a "promotion" which the highly productive worker must himself ask for. Some of those compensated for piecework earn as much as $3 per hour. Typical earnings, however, come to no more than $15 or $20 per week, and in the case of welfare or other third-party payment patients, this money is often used to pay for supplies in the occupational therapy shop.

Rehabilitation. Although many of the day patients have a history of mental illness, a relatively small proportion are seriously regressed or impaired in terms of social skills and job capabilities. Consequently there is relatively little specific focus on improving social behavior or training for employment.

Boarding. Day patients who become agitated can be placed temporarily on the inpatient service, provided a bed is available, as often there is not. Rarely would there be more than one or two day patients being temporarily boarded on the inpatient service, and usually there are none. One or two patients at any given time may be in foster homes in the community.

Family involvement. Family members are typically interviewed at the time of admission. Many of the day patients are brought to the hospital by relatives, who sometimes remain at the day center in the morning or come early in the afternoon in order to discuss the patient's condition with the nurse. The staff encourage this practice. Home visits are very rarely made.

Disposition. We have indicated that in 1967, fifteen, or about seventeen percent of day patients, were transferred to inpatient status, and the principal reason why.

Of 73 other patients separated from day hospital status during 1967, more than half (53 percent) were transferred to outpatient status, illustrating once more that the day hospital is perceived principally as a transitional facility for the person who is making gains following inpatient treatment. An additional 23 patients (32 percent) were released without provision for further treatment. Six were transferred to Topeka State Hospital; these were patients *a*) who were admitted to day care because no inpatient beds were available, *b*) whose need for longer-term inpatient care became evident, and *c*) who lacked funds to pay for inpatient care at Prairie View.

Outcome. This facility, like most others that we know of, has not conducted formal outcome investigations of patients who have been discharged from treatment.

Records

Complete records are kept for day patients. Two of the consultants reviewed a random selection of records and found them to be of high quality.

Transportation

Prairie View is located at one edge of Newton, a town of 16,000 which has no local bus service. Occasional day patients have walked to the hospital or come by taxi. For other patients, unless they can drive their own cars or have relatives to drive them, getting to Prairie View is pretty well out of the question. The outlying county seats are 27 and 35 miles from the hospital, and there is virtually no public transportation.

Agency relationships

It would appear that the welfare program will pay the costs of hospitalization in some components of the Prairie View program inasmuch as there is strong federal participation. We interviewed the representatives of the local welfare department and found them to be well acquainted with the hospital and sympathetic to the preferability of local treatment for mental illness. They indicated that funds were usually readily available to meet the cost of day hospital treatment for welfare clients although representatives of the center indicated there had been some problems in getting coverage.

Placements

Prairie View does not recruit jobs for patients. However, the nurse in charge of the day center meets monthly with the personnel managers of two firms where former day patients are employed.

The nurse also has found boarding homes for occasional patients. There is a halfway house in Newton of evidently high quality, and occasional patients have lived there while participating in the day program.

Financing

In their efforts to provide comprehensive service, the conscientious and dedicated staff and administration of this outstanding community program are seriously hampered by the limitations set by the mental health boards of the three counties that it serves. None of the three will pay for inpatient treatment, so that persons who on the one hand cannot qualify for welfare assistance and on the other do not have health insurance or private funds to pay for care are necessarily transferred to Topeka State Hospital.

The two adjacent counties will pay for day treatment, but Harvey County, in which Prairie View is located, cannot with the limited funds allowed by the county commissioners.

Blue Cross covers day treatment to the same extent that it covers inpatient treatment—thirty days per year. So do some of the commercial insurance plans, but a number of others do not.

Despite the fact that Prairie View is a private facility that has a very small endowment and is obliged to break even financially, it bends every effort to provide appropriate treatment even in the face of this patchwork financial picture. Any emergency is accepted, although inevitably those who must have inpatient care for more than a few days and are unable to pay must be transferred to the state hospital.

Various inventive approaches are used for the day patients. A number of them come only one or two half-days per week, in some cases purely as a financial expedient, when therapeutic indications would make more frequent attendance preferable. Day patients with limited funds are encouraged to choose less expensive projects in the activities therapies. They are also given the opportunity to earn money in the industrial therapy program so that they can pay for activities and in some cases help defray the cost of treatment.

The charge in the day hospital is $16 for a full day, $8 for a half-day, including group therapy. Psychotherapy is charged at $22.50 per hour and psychodrama at $4 per session.

Future plans

Dr. Jones feels that the day program is still under development and that in time it will involve larger numbers of patients. Obviously this will require finding the way to overcome problems of transportation and money. The day program did not seem to us to be fully integrated conceptually into the total program; to the extent that this is so, it probably results from the fact that *a*) Prairie View has grown steadily and rapidly in the past several years without the advantage of a "settling in" period, *b*) the day hospital has had its own quarters only a short time and still has very little staff of its own, and *c*) day patients go to the outpatient building for individual appointments rather than the staff moving into the day hospital. However, there was none of the resistance to day care as such that we have encountered in some other programs. From this very large and sparsely settled area, there are more day patients than in a number of mental health centers that we know of in central areas of major cities. Despite Dr. Jones' ambition to use the day program more frequently as a means of obviating 24-hour care, Prairie View's day hospital may already be approaching the optimum capacity. Obviously there comes a point of demarcation beyond which problems of transportation outweigh the advantages that partial hospitalization offers over 24-hour treatment.

Syracuse Psychiatric Hospital
Syracuse, New York

S YRACUSE PSYCHIATRIC HOSPITAL was established in the 1930's as a typical small psychopathic hospital. With sixty beds, it provided principally inpatient treatment to patients from anywhere in New York State, selected according to the facility's teaching needs.

In 1966, when Dr. John Cumming was director, the facility was transformed into a pilot and demonstration community mental health center to develop data that would be useful to the New York State Department of Mental Hygiene in its program to establish mental health centers throughout the state.* Its policy of admitting selected patients from a wide area for intermediate and long-term care was supplanted by an inclusive admission policy for all of the persons living in a catchment that comprises slightly more than one third of the population of Onondaga County.

To delineate the catchment, a sociogram was drawn up of the entire county, showing the economic, ethnic, mental illness, and other characteristics of its 390,000 residents. Because of the research interests of Syracuse Psychiatric Hospital (SPH), an effort was made to divide the county in such a way as to provide the most stabilized area for its program and also one that would provide a representative socioeconomic cross section. The area designated has a population of 170,000. Presumably the two remaining portions of the county will eventually have their own community mental health centers.

The SPH catchment has been subdivided further into three areas, each having a treatment team and a unit (ward) within the program. The number of beds was reduced to 45, divided into three 15-bed units. Provision for partial hospitalization within the inpatient service was added in mid-1966, and an outpatient service was added in mid-1967. Patients from the catchment may be seen in emergency at any time

---

*Although the demonstration program received approximately $500,000 in federal funds, these funds came from the Hospital Improvement Project; Syracuse Psychiatric Hospital is not funded under the 1963 federal Community Mental Health Centers Act.

by center personnel. Walk-in emergencies from outside the catchment area are also evaluated by center personnel, who take the responsibility of arranging treatment elsewhere. Each team provides consultants to agencies in their particular areas, including social agencies, health facilities, and other hospitals who have admitted patients from the SPH catchment. It was the view of the consultants that the facility had made important progress towards its goal, and that the program promises to yield useful and much-needed information about community-based services for the mentally ill. It will attempt to answer such basic questions as the number of inpatient beds needed for a given unit of population.

In the days prior to the community mental health center program, there were never more than eight to ten day patients for the entire hospital. All of the patients on day status at the time of the change-over in programs were assigned to one of the three teams.

It is important to realize that the city of Syracuse has numerous psychiatric resources. There are two voluntary general hospitals that have psychiatric units, both of which provide contract service to the state. There is an adult outpatient clinic that sees about 120 persons per week, and a child guidance clinic. The state hospital serving Onondaga County is Marcy State Hospital, about forty miles from Syracuse. Thus, even though the SPH program serves all of the residents of its catchment who seek its service, there are those living there who are eligible to be served elsewhere if they prefer—which, by custom, some do—and there are others who have the means for private care. As of the time of our visit, a number of persons continued to be hospitalized at Marcy, although very few of them—less than ten in a one-year period—were transfers from SPH. However, about 150 persons from the catchment area had gone directly to Marcy, some as voluntary patients, others on certificates from health officers. Of this 150, however, half or more were from categories of patients that are not admitted at SPH: children under sixteen, alcoholics, criminal order cases, and the severely physically debilitated. As for those who would have been eligible, the staff saw as one of their early needs a campaign to educate the various agencies involved in hospitalizing the mentally ill to send every such person to SPH.

Physical plant

Syracuse Psychiatric Hospital occupies all of a four-story brick building located in the Upstate Medical Center complex. About 35 years old, the building gives a somewhat timeworn but comfortable and commodious feeling. Each of the three upper floors houses a ward and also has offices for the staff.

The program also uses two nearby frame houses, one for the geriatric day program, the other for occupational therapy activities. There is also an outpatient satellite, located in a storefront one mile from the hospital, in a racially mixed and densely populated neighborhood with a high crime rate. This satellite, staffed by an indigenous worker, also serves as an information and referral center.

Capacity and range of census

The stated day patient capacity was 85. During 1967 the range was from five to 43 persons per day. During a week in mid-January 1968, 51 persons were seen as day patients. The number has continued to increase and as of early June 1968 the enrollment had reached one hundred. The eventual limit had not been set as of that time.

The staff

The most significant and interesting aspect of the staffing pattern in this facility is that patients are assigned to a particular staff team rather than to the inpatient, outpatient, or day services. Thus, each team has at any given time some patients on each of these statuses. This sensible, readily accomplished, but uncommon practice builds into a program a continuity of treatment that cannot possibly be as well accomplished in any other fashion.

Each of the three teams has a high degree of autonomy and therefore there are some differences among them in constituency. But each team has responsibility for 15 inpatient beds, approximately 25 day patients, 25 outpatients, and 25 aftercare patients. (The latter two categories are distinguished as follows: if an inpatient at SPH is transferred to outpatient status, he is considered to be an aftercare patient; if he has not been an inpatient during the current episode of illness, even though he may have been at some earlier time, he is considered to be an outpatient.)

An "average" team is composed of a psychiatrist, either full time or three-quarters time, three social workers, six nurses, twelve attendants, one occupational therapist, one recreational therapist, and one resident. This can be seen as a very rich staff-patient ratio, partly because of the relative newness of the program and the fact that it has expanded gradually rather than all at once. The demand for service had increased considerably during the months prior to our visit without any increase in staff, so that the initially quite rich staffing pattern had already become somewhat thinner. It seemed likely that as demand continued to increase and as additional types of service were introduced, the staffing would become even thinner.

Each patient is assigned a "primary therapist," who may be any member of the staff. Indeed, a number of patients have had nursing attendants as their primary therapists. This has led to resistance only in a few cases, perhaps principally because this person plays an "advocate" role more than a traditional psychotherapeutic role. As described to us, the primary therapist system seemed to have some of the characteristics of the "buddy system." A given patient might or might not, in time of trouble, turn to his primary therapist, but in any case the primary therapist is always available to him.

On two of the three teams, all of the staff are involved in the therapeutic milieu with all of the patients. This is true of the third team, up to a point, but an important modification has been introduced: certain members of the team have been designated a sort of "sub-team" to concentrate on day patients. This was felt to be necessary after it became evident that many day patients were being lost in the shuffle, or at least that they felt they were. This stems from the early days of the community mental health center program when the inpatient service from which it was developed continued to be the prestigious service, not only because it was the first but because it had the sickest patients.* Consequently, the day patients floundered, and many of them simply would not come. Thus, two nursing attendants and two nurses were given special responsibility for the day patients, with a modest amount of separate activity scheduled for them. At the time of our visit, a second team was considering making the same arrangement.

All of the streets and housing developments in the catchment are listed in a directory. During daytime hours, whenever an applicant for service is presented at the switchboard, the telephone operator consults the directory to determine which team is responsible for the patient; she calls the designated "officer of the day" for that team, who comes to interview the patient and determines which level of service he requires, if any. The officer-of-the-day assignment rotates among the residents, social workers, and nurses. In the evening the officer of the day is a resident who makes the decision for the team.

---

*This appears to be a commonplace attitude in programs that have a major interest in the inpatient service. It is in curious contrast to outpatient clinics, where it appears to be most prestigious to have a caseload of highly articulate neurotic patients.

A number of the present staff worked at the hospital prior to its community mental health center program. There was no special formal training to acquaint them with the new operation, other than considerable discussion involving all personnel during the months preceding the change-over to a catchment-based mental health center. Said one of the staff psychiatrists, "During the first eighteen months we had intensive inservice training and supervision to enable the staff to become much more involved with patient care, and following that we began to emphasize the ways in which they can become more involved with the community."

Each team meets five mornings a week for a staff meeting that is, in effect, a regular morning report. One morning a week the meeting is scheduled early enough to allow the night staff to stay on and join in.

Volunteers are extensively used. There is a full-time director of volunteers, who supervises approximately eighty hours per week of volunteer activities. Much of this is time donated by students, particularly those who intend to major in sociology or psychology. There are also women from the community. The volunteers involve the patients in art classes, cooking, dressmaking, operating a beauty shop, and doing volunteer work. They teach Yoga and lip reading. They sometimes provide transportation. They assist the staff with psychodrama, occupational therapy, and recreation, and spend time socializing with the patients.

Referrals

Of two hundred persons who were placed on partial hospitalization status during 1967, two thirds were transfers from the SPH inpatient service. Under the existing pattern, this simply means that the person who had been an inpatient began to spend his evenings and weekends at home, while returning to the hospital five or fewer days per week to participate in the same program as the inpatients.

There were an additional seven patients (four percent) who were transferred to day status at SPH from other hospitals. These were long-term, socially regressed patients especially selected from Marcy State Hospital for a day care program planned by Dr. Philip P. Steckler of the Syracuse Psychiatric Hospital staff. It was necessary for the mental health center personnel to investigate the family of each prospective day patient and discuss with them the possibility of assuming responsibility at night and on weekends. Although only seven families, or about one fifth of those contacted, agreed to have their relatives enter the program, it had not been necessary to return any of the seven patients to full-time hospitalization.

Other referrals during 1967 were as follows:

Self-referred	9%
SPH outpatient service	6
Private physicians	5
Outpatient services other than SPH	5
Private psychiatrists	2
Public Health nurses	2
Family and friends	2
Welfare department	1

Selection procedure

The categories of patients excluded at SPH are persons under sixteen years of age, alcoholics without psychosis, criminal order cases, and the severely physically debilitated. Beyond these exclusions, any person is eligible for admission as a day patient provided the officer of the day, after examining him, decides that day status is an appropriate intensity of care. In given cases this determination will obviously include such considerations as ambulation and family situation. We suspected that there was some conservatism when the choice lay between inpatient and day status, possibly a holdover from the fairly recent days when the facility provided only inpatient care. Various members of the staff anticipated that when the pressure for inpatient beds increases, there will be a larger number of admissions direct to day status.

Characteristics of the patients

A research unit was established shortly after the change-over in 1966 to consider especially such aspects of the patient population as history of mental illness, previous state hospitalization, and socioeconomic characteristics. This unit is composed of a psychiatrist, business administrator, anthropologist, two research staff, and a secretary.

The catchment is somewhat weighted with people from the lower socioeconomic groups. Half of the day patients had been previously treated in New York's state mental hospitals, including in some cases Syracuse Psychiatric Hospital.

During 1967, slightly more than a quarter of the patients on day status were men (27 percent). The substantial majority—85 percent—

were between 21 and 65, while the rest were evenly divided between those over 65 and those between 16 and 21.

The modal diagnosis was schizophrenia, accounting for 34 percent. Other diagnoses were as follows:

Psychoneurotic disorders	20%
Personality disorders	15
Psychotic depressions	10
Chronic brain syndromes	9
All others	11

During the eighteen months since day care had been instituted, a "hard core" group of chronic schizophrenics had built up, accounting for approximately 25 percent of the patients altogether. Half of these patients, although having a long illness at the time, had no history of previous severe illness. Dr. James Prevost, coordinator of clinical program and training, thinks this probably indicates that SPH is holding onto a group of patients which a short-term hospital would have transferred elsewhere at an earlier date. This "silting up" phenomenon has been seen in other programs, including, notably, the Fort Logan Mental Health Center. It will be interesting to observe, as the SPH program gains further operating experience, the extent of this silting up, and the means adopted to attempt to deal with it.

The average length of stay for persons released from day status during 1967 was 72 days. This includes many persons who were transferred from inpatient status, for which the average stay during 1967 was 32 days. Consequently, the total combined inpatient-day status average stay for a number of patients comes to 104 days, which is quite long for community-based services. Furthermore, it does not reflect the particularly long-stay patient still in the program, since length-of-stay figures are based on released patients.

Treatment philosophy

The treatment program was described by one of the psychiatrists as "a transactional model." He and various other persons we interviewed emphasized the group aspects of treatment. Despite the fact that each patient has some staff person designated as his primary therapist, the principal business of the program is seen as taking place in the treatment milieu. Said one of the social workers, "The people who come here as patients have problems in relating to other people, and we force and foster situations in which they have to deal with problems and situations that involve other people. This aspect of treatment is important throughout the program and accounts for our major emphasis on group therapy, on psychodrama, on activities together. It means that the staff have to be very active in confronting people and to be very alert to handle problems as they arise instead of letting everyone sit in silence."

One of the psychiatrists said, "Our most severe problem comes after the acute problem has been dealt with. Our goal is to enable the patient to function in the community, however marginally. Consequently, we don't see the day patients who are 'silting up' as failures. Many of them were in and out of the state hospital regularly, every few months, over a period of many years. Some of them, by coming in for two or three days a week, have been sustained by our day program for a period of eighteen months."

The emphasis in psychotherapy was said to be directed toward the patient's immediate relationships and to his relationships with the community and on the job. One of the staff said, "It can't be called insight therapy in the sense of exploring infantile neuroses, but it's insight in the sense of giving the patient some knowledge about the difficulties he's having and the faulty ways he's been relating to his environment." In response to our inquiry, various staff members, including psychiatrists, said that there is very little staff activity other than overseeing medication that seemed to require the exclusive competence of the psychiatrist.

The treatment program

Dr. Prevost aptly compared the SPH treatment program to "a store." "We tell the patient what we have to sell, and he finds out what he wants to buy," Dr. Prevost said. "If someone starts out with us as an outpatient and it then appears that he needs more time in the program, we certainly try to persuade him to come more often. On the other hand, if we reach an agreement with the patient that he should come to the day hospital for three days each week and he doesn't come, we ask him what's going on, and we discuss whether it's necessary to make a different agreement."

In effect, then, the treatment program spans a continuum all the way from 24-hour care seven days per week down to infrequent outpatient appointments for drug regulation. We have already seen that the pattern of staff assignment allows for complete continuity of care in terms of therapeutic personnel; in addition, the range of care allows continuity in terms of intensity, without resort to arbitrary delineations between services, as is the case in most treatment facilities.

Most patients are seen individually, mainly in supportive psychotherapy, by their primary therapists, most of whom are residents, social workers, nurses, and attendants. These sessions may take place quite infrequently and principally at the patient's request, or they may take place daily for a limited period of time for particular patients. A few patients are involved in intensive, psychoanalytically oriented therapy with residents under the supervision of the staff psychiatrists.

Most patients also participate in group psychotherapy, again led most often by social workers, nurses, and aides. These one-hour sessions take place typically two times per week. The majority of patients are on light dosages of psychotropic medications. The drugs are dispensed at the hospital, usually one week's supply at a time.

All of the patients participate in recreational and occupational therapy. In the course of a typical week these activities will include calisthenics, a slide lecture, a bowling tournament, creative dancing, a poetry discussion, a card tournament, swimming, cooking, roller skating, a songfest, and a movie.

Each week there are also two psychodrama sessions, a patient government meeting, and a community meeting.

Work-for-pay. As of the time of our visit no work-for-pay program had been developed.

Boarding. Boarding of upset day patients overnight is usually possible, but occurs infrequently.

Family involvement. More than two thirds of the patients' families are seen, but in the majority of cases it is largely a matter of exchanging information. For approximately fifteen percent, there is an ongoing relationship with the team, which in some cases is clearly defined as therapy. This therapy has taken the form of weekly spouse groups, family groups, conjoint therapy, and in some cases, individual therapy.

Home visits. Home visits are made as needed, often by the nurses. The frequency is high, averaging fifty visits per month for all mental health center patients. In mid-1968 one of the clinical teams began visiting the homes of almost all of its patients. The principal reason for visiting the home is to learn more about the patient's specific environment. The practice is part of the overall philosophy of involvement with the total patient. Home visits are also made because of temporary physical debility of patients or occasionally to evaluate an uncooperative patient.

Disposition. Among 134 patients who were released from partial hospitalization status during 1967, the largest group, 58 persons, or 43 percent, were released without provision for further treatment. The next largest group, 53, or 40 percent, were transferred to outpatient status within SPH. Sixteen patients, or 12 percent, were transferred to inpatient status at SPH, and the remaining seven patients were referred or transferred to several other facilities.

Outcome. Among the patients released from day status during 1967, seven percent were considered to be in remission at the time of release; 72 percent were considered improved; 18 percent were considered unimproved; and three percent left the program against medical advice.

This program had not undertaken follow-up studies to determine how patients were faring after a period of time away from treatment. One hopes that this will be done, since the research and demonstration aspects of this program will lend particular pertinence to outcome figures.

It is important to note the very low rate of transfer from this relatively short-term treatment program to the state hospital. Only two patients on day status were transferred to the state hospital during the course of a year, and only about six patients altogether. Each one was a severe and intractable case that presented gross management problems. This very low transfer rate is encouraging. One looks to the time when this program evolves to the point of intercepting all of those persons within its catchment who are now presented directly to the state hospital. More than most other facilities that we know of, this one is in a position to determine what percentage of the mentally ill can be maintained successfully in a short-term community-based treatment program.

The geriatric program

This is one of two among the programs we visited that provides a special day program for geriatric patients.

Originally all day patients were grouped together, but it soon became evident that the active and highly scheduled program was too strenuous for various older patients who seemed otherwise suitable for day treatment. Consequently all day patients over the age of 65 were separated off. (Since then patients have been considered for the geriatric program on the basis of degree of organic impairment and not simply by age. Consequently there are some "young" elderly patients on the regular clinical teams and there are some "elderly" 50-year-olds in the geriatric program.) The chief social worker was particularly assigned to develop a program for them. This program takes place in a frame residence located near the main building. The treatment philosophy and the activities do not differ essentially from that of the regular day program, except that less physical exertion is required and a slower pace is maintained. While the numbers involved had not been great up to the time of our visit, the staff had found that such patients can be very suitably cared for on day status. During 1967, only five of these geriatric day patients required transfer to inpatient care, and each of them was returned a short time later to day status.

Night hospital

At any given time there are a few patients on night status, the substantial majority of whom are persons who were inpatients who returned to their jobs but who need a supportive transition period. At the time of our visit there were nine persons on night status. They participate in the same evening activities as the inpatients.

Transportation

Transportation for day patients poses little problem since there is ample public bus transportation. Some come from as far away as fifteen miles. Patients on welfare arrive by taxi, subsidized by that agency.

Transportation is provided for day care patients in the geriatric day care program. A bus owned by the hospital picks these patients up each morning and returns them to their homes in the afternoon.

Agency relationships

Many of the clinical personnel spend some portion of their time with other agencies in working out plans for the patients. Among these are the welfare department, the Public Health nurses, the Syracuse Housing Authority, the state employment service, the Division of Vocational Rehabilitation, a sheltered workshop called Consolidated Industries, and various departments of the Upstate Medical Center.

"Because our patients move to and from partial hospitalization status frequently and freely, it's difficult for us to separate out the extent of our efforts for partial hospitalization patients," said Dr. Prevost. "In any case, it's one of the more important facets of our program." Generally it is the policy of the mental health center staff to offer information and make suggestions about jobs or living arrangements but to leave the responsibility for making contacts up to the patient or his family. At the time of our visit SPH had no family care homes or halfway houses under its jurisdiction, although halfway houses were considered an important project for the future. Nursing home placements were extremely difficult because of long waiting lists. In 1967 two patients were placed in nursing homes and three in proprietary homes. Mental health center staff make many referrals to the state employment service but generally leave it to the patient to do the footwork. During 1967, ten patients were accepted by a sheltered workshop facility. An additional twelve patients were successfully placed in regular jobs through the direct efforts of the center staff. These twelve were still employed by mid-1968. Three others were placed in vocational training programs.

Financing

It is in respect of budget that the SPH program is perhaps most fortunate. With ample funds provided by the state and the NIMH grant, there has been no need to skimp or improvise because of lack of money and there has been no pressure to discharge patients because of financial considerations. No fees are levied for any treatment except inpatient care, and even there the ability to pay plays no part in whether the patient is accepted for treatment. The program has not been functioning long enough as a community mental health center to be able to provide detailed financial statistics. These figures, when they become available, will be of particular interest to those involved in mental health planning.

Future plans

Said Dr. Prevost, "Future center plans are concerned with two major areas: the 'silting up' problem and primary prevention. Establishment of a halfway house has already been studied, and we hope to have it in operation in a structure four blocks from the center by mid-1969."

He added, "It should be noted that all of the services have been provided to the catchment with no waiting list. The next objective is to move day care and outpatient services largely to satellite units in the team areas. For some months negotiations have been carried on with the county, state, and Syracuse University authorities to plan satellite units in the housing developments located in our area. Operations are beginning in one unit collaborating with the Family Service Center. This satellite provides day care and outpatient service to the aged and also acts as a general referral service for the population in the immediate vicinity. We are planning a more ambitious project in a high-rise geriatric building, where we plan to have space for a fully equipped and staffed day care unit for the elderly. We feel that eventually most of our day care patients can be moved from the Syracuse Psychiatric Hospital to the satellite units in their own areas.

"As for primary prevention, we hope to establish two new store-front outpatient and information referral centers. These are planned for multi-problem inner-city populations. We hope to have neighborhood people working in these centers."

Mt. Sinai Hospital
New York City

M T. SINAI HOSPITAL, with 1337 beds, is one of the largest voluntary general hospitals in the United States, and its psychiatry service, with 123 beds, is one of the country's largest general hospital psychiatric services. The hospital is located in Manhattan's upper East Side, in a neighborhood that has about equal proportions of luxury apartments and dilapidated, overcrowded tenements.

The psychiatry service is located in the Klingenstein Clinical Center, a modern nine-story building that was completed in 1962. The outpatient division is located on the first floor, the inpatient division occupies the seventh and eighth floors, and the Day and Night Center occupies a portion of the sixth floor. One member of the staff aptly described the psychiatry service as "a hospital within a hospital."

The psychiatry service has as full-time administrative staff its director, Dr. M. Ralph Kaufman, a coordinator of patient services, and the chief psychologist. Each division and unit is headed up by a half-time attending psychiatrist. Each of these men also participates in the extensive psychiatric residency training program. As one might expect of so large a program within so large a hospital, the organization is extremely complex. It should suffice in this context to point out that the largest divisions are child psychiatry, inpatient adult psychiatry, outpatient adult psychiatry, liaison services, training, and department-wide divisions of social work and psychology. The "day unit" and "night unit" are designated as two of the seven subdivisions of the adult inpatient division.

The physical plant

The completely separate day-night center is housed in attractive and adequate quarters. Two large rooms fitted with foldaway beds are used as activity rooms during the day and evening and as the men's and women's dormitories at night. There are also a kitchen, a dining room, and a dayroom. The day-night center uses the gymnasium, library, and

150

occupational therapy and rehabilitation facilities that serve the entire psychiatry department and in some cases the entire hospital.

Capacity and range of census

The day, evening, and night hospitalization units were opened in 1963, with the same capacity as at the time of our visit in March 1968. The stated capacity of the day hospital is 40, the evening hospital, 20, the night hospital, 22. During 1967 the census in the day hospital ranged from 17 to 32, in the evening hospital from three to six, in the night hospital from 15 to 21. In all three cases the census was very substantially affected by the availability and policies of third-party payments, as described below.

The staff

The full-time staff of the Day and Night Center include:

- 5 psychiatric residents
- 2 social workers (one for day unit, one for night unit)
- 10 registered nurses
- 3 attendants
- 2 recreational therapists (one for day unit, one for night unit)
- 1 occupational therapist
- 2 unit clerks (one for day unit, one for night unit)

The part-time staff include the director, Dr. Samuel Feder, on a half-time basis, a three-quarter-time staff psychiatrist, a quarter-time psychologist, a half-time social worker, and a half-time aide. The chief resident, Dr. Allan Beigel, spends substantially full time in this service, in addition to limited duties in the outpatient division and participation in the extensive formal teaching program.

All of the staff persons that we interviewed appeared to be well trained and highly motivated. They are components of a treatment team with overlapping roles. All of them are involved in the overall treatment of the patient (and his family), with each bringing the additional skills characteristic of his or her special training. The social workers work directly with the patients and individual family members to secure services from agencies in a variety of nonpsychiatric areas. Patients are encouraged to be involved in these requests for services although it is often necessary for social service to intervene. About 75 percent of the patients need and receive assistance in securing nonpsychiatric services in the community.

On a day-to-day basis, it is the registered nurses who work most closely with the patients. They have the most contact with the patients during their time in the hospital and are involved with them daily on individual matters and interpersonal situations as they arise. They are part of all activities (in and out of the hospital), and they participate in some group meetings and lead others. They convey significant material to the physician and receive such information in return. They contact the patients who do not come in and frequently make home visits (alone, with the social worker, or with the doctor) for evaluation purposes or to help with crises outside the hospital.

In this hospital, while the psychiatric nursing service is administratively a subsection of the hospital-wide nursing service, it has an independent philosophy attuned to the needs of the department of psychiatry. It would be an additional advantage to have the Day and Night Center nursing staff free of certain general departmental policies.

The activity therapists spend considerable time with the patients, attend various group meetings and group therapy, and in addition to their own special duties, have many informal one-to-one discussions with patients.

All members of the staff are in frequent daily communication and all members of the team attend and participate actively in the daily staff meetings.

The staff seemed to agree that the essence of their program was a multiple group approach, involving both formal group therapy, group activity therapy, and unit meetings.

Volunteers have rarely been used; there has been occasional instruction in bridge, music appreciation, etc.

Referrals

Slightly more than 325 persons were on partial hospitalization status during 1967. They were referred from a variety of sources, as follows:

Private psychiatrists	30%
Mt. Sinai inpatient service	18
Mt. Sinai emergency room—direct	18
Mt. Sinai outpatient psychiatry division	12
Community agencies	11
Other hospitals	5
General practitioners	2
Self-referred by telephone	2
Psychologists in private practice	1

The chief resident examines each person referred to determine whether he is a suitable candidate for any of the partial hospitalization services. Most patients, especially those in the night hospital, are admitted directly to that service.

Selection procedure

Assuming the availability of resources to pay for the treatment, there are a number of additional criteria used to determine whether an applicant should be admitted to the partial hospitalization service. Specifically:

• He must not use drugs or alcohol on the unit and must not come into the program so much under the influence of drugs or alcohol as to be unable to participate in the program.

• He must be able to arrange his own transportation to and from home, or else must have a family member or friend who will do so.

• He must attend according to the schedule considered therapeutic by the staff.

• If a day patient, he must have a suitable place to stay at night; if a night patient, he must be in school, employed, or actively looking or training for work.

• If his family lives in the vicinity, he must assent to the involvement of relatives in the program to the extent the treatment staff think appropriate.

• He must be able to observe "minimal rules necessary to the running of a hospital, because disruptive behavior is contagious, especially in the night hospital."

• If he lacks impulse control or is too psychotically disorganized, he may be kept on the Day and Night Center, on 24-hour status, up to one week. If during that time there is not sufficient response to medication and other treatment he is transferred to the 24-hour service. At any time during the stay, he may spend some time on 24-hour status in the Day and Night Center.

It is interesting to note that with this rather extensive list of criteria the program does not exclude patients who pose a suicide risk.

Characteristics of the patients

Since Mt. Sinai does not serve a prescribed catchment and can accept patients from all of New York City (or, for those who can pay, from any city or state) the patients are a mixed group. There are upper- and middle-class persons of mixed background, and poor persons, mainly of

Negro and Puerto Rican backgrounds. There have been those living on "unearned income," physicians, and scholars, as well as those who have been financially, educationally, and culturally deprived. There are almost twice as many women as men (64 percent vs. 36 percent). Almost three quarters of the patients (73 percent) are between 21 and 65 years old. Only five percent are over 65. Twenty-two percent are under 21, the majority of them night patients who go to school during the daytime; it is the general policy of the program not to accept adolescents in the day unit, on the grounds that it is not suitable to impose on them, in addition to their roles at home and in school, a third role of day hospital patient.

Numerical breakdowns by diagnosis were not furnished to us. Dr. Feder indicated that most of the patients on partial hospitalization status are persons either with *a*) acute schizophrenic reactions, *b*) chronic schizophrenic reactions with or without severe depression, or *c*) character disorders. "There are also a fair number of severe hysterical reactions, especially among the Puerto Rican patients, also with depression as an important aspect," he said. "At all times we have several patients who are preoccupied with suicide; the danger of suicide has to be dealt with daily."

Dr. Feder does not feel that formal diagnosis is very often the crucial criterion. "It is rather a matter of what remnants of healthy ego the patient has, and whether there is enough impulse control and integration so that one can make meaningful contact with him," he said.

The tendency of the patient to regress is seen as an important obstacle that must be overcome in treatment. "The patients who come here, if left to their own devices, will fade into the woodwork or will continue in their same destructive and unsatisfactory patterns," Dr. Feder said. "They will isolate themselves, remain inactive, accept no challenge, move into no new areas of interest. They don't want to be stirred up. Their defenses and their maladaptive behavior are rigid. One of our continuing problems is to keep people involved. If we don't maintain a constant effort, the patients will either drift off into their own little worlds or will come out for a skirmish and then retreat again."

When asked what would happen to the current caseload of patients if the partial hospitalization services were discontinued, Dr. Feder said that some would require transfer to 24-hour care, while others could be maintained as outpatients. However, he found it difficult to anticipate what the proportion would be of each.

He indicated that the program is interested in learning whether there are patients for whom partial hospitalization is the treatment of choice, and he believes that the Mt. Sinai night hospital patients may constitute such a group. "These are the patients who can benefit from really knowledgeable and integrated group activity and therapy, at a frequency of two or three times a week, far more than they would benefit from two or three individual therapy sessions per week."

Mt. Sinai imposes a stricter schedule on its partial hospitalization patients than most of the other programs we visited, for reasons that are described later. However, it is pertinent to put forward here Dr. Feder's perception of the patient characteristics that can disrupt a program where patients may come and go rather freely. "We have had patients who attempt to 'mold the hospital,'" he said, "particularly those with acting-out and impulsive tendencies. They try to structure the time they are here according to their personal patterns. For instance, we have group therapy three evenings a week from six thirty to seven thirty; some patients will say, 'Well, I can't get here until eight.' We expect our day patients to be here before nine o'clock each morning, and there are patients who will say, 'I can't get up in time to get here before ten thirty.' We have others who are supposed to stay until three thirty, and they want to leave at one. At the outset, we told ourselves that we would go along with individual needs and try to work things out to everyone's satisfaction. But we found that the exceptions became epidemic. When a single outspoken and exhibitionist patient began to disregard the schedule, there would soon be a second one and a third one, and before long half of the patients were coming in too late for group therapy. The sense of cohesiveness was lost.

"We're also quite direct with behavior that disrupts the program. We don't try to dictate to our patients what they will do when they're not here. However, if a patient comes in roaring drunk every night, we tell him that he can stop drinking early enough in the day so that he can be involved when he's here, or else we tell him to stop coming. We can help the person who is hallucinating or delusional, but we can't and won't put up with his violent temper when it is put into action against others; such a patient may well have to be transferred to 24-hour care. We've learned the hard way that with partial hospitalization one doesn't have the same kind of therapeutic control over his patients that he has on a 24-hour service."

As with other programs in New York City, there were both cultural and language problems with Puerto Rican patients. "They tend to stay together a great deal," one of the activity therapists told us. "They do a lot of cooking and sewing—more than the middle-class patients, who do more 'creative' things. Most of the time the Puerto Rican patients remain silent in group activities, but it's not so much that they can't speak English as that they use the language difference as an excuse for not participating. However, we are beginning to experience some success, particularly with the young Puerto Rican girls. Their cultural and environmental deprivation is long-standing, but through some of the activities here we do get through to them."

Relatively few of the patients either on day or night status have been hospitalized in state hospitals. The staff felt that on the whole the day patients were more chronic, more regressed, and less responsive than the night patients, who were described by Dr. Feder as "the healthiest" among all the Mt. Sinai psychiatric patients.

The length of stay is related to the financial resources available, as described below. During 1967 the distribution by length of stay was as follows:

	Day patients	Night patients
Less than 2 weeks	22%	10%
2- 4 weeks	14	21
4- 6 weeks	7	8
6- 8 weeks	6	6
8-10 weeks	10	7
10-12 weeks	36	44
More than 12 weeks	5	4

Treatment philosophy

This program might be most accurately described as one that had its origins in individual psychotherapy and is at present in transition toward a focus on group process. Most of the psychiatric staff at Mt. Sinai are psychoanalysts (including the director of the Day and Night Center), and the training program there has traditionally stressed the one-to-one psychiatrist-patient relationship. The residents are said to choose this training program usually because they are most interested in individual treatment. The transition has as its goal an integrated program utilizing the milieu, group activity, group therapy, and individual therapy. Each of the private patients, who comprise about sixteen percent of the total, continues to be seen individually by his private psychiatrist, and each of the service patients is assigned to a psychiatric resident who is responsible for overseeing his total treatment. Group activity and group therapy are the main foci of treatment. But all the patients are seen individually at least once a week; when necessary, or when it is considered therapeutically beneficial, they are seen twice a week (rarely three times).

Dr. Feder made the point that it is important to know what is happening in the inner life of the patient as well as in the outward, behavioral life, since the two are often intimately and causally related. The individual meetings, he feels, offer the best way to learn this. He feels that the most well-rounded treatment program will obtain and integrate knowledge and experience from all contacts the patient has with other patients, staff, and individual therapist.

The staff persons we interviewed consistently referred to the program as a therapeutic community, but it was difficult to see that this was so in terms of the therapeutic community concept put forward by Dr. Maxwell Jones. It appeared more suitable to refer to the group emphasis in this program as a therapeutic milieu.

This program appeared to fall more within the medical model than most of the others that we visited. This is by design. For example, the nursing station was locked when unattended (as the result of hospital-wide policy). Staff members wear name tags but patients do not. There are different toilets for staff, patients, and visitors. And while nurses do not wear uniforms, all of the other staff, including the administrative assistant to the chief of psychiatry, wear white coats.

The treatment program

This was the only partial hospitalization program we visited that operates seven days a week. There appear to be two principal reasons why it does. In planning the service it was assumed there would be a substantial demand for weekend hospitalization (but this did not develop, partly because the New York City Community Mental Health Board will not pay for it, but largely because there turned out to be little call for it). Also, because of certain aspects of Community Mental Health Board reimbursement regulations, there is a limited period of time in which to work with the patient and consequently it is felt important to involve him as intensively as possible. There is somewhat more free time allowed in the Saturday and Sunday schedule, and the staffing is somewhat lighter on those days, but even so the program is structured as a full-time affair. Said Dr. Feder, "The administrative involvement with the general hospital dictates the seven-day utilization and staffing pattern. In addition, night patients generally require and prefer this arrangement. Sunday night is one of the most important in the night hospital."

There are group therapy sessions as the first activity on three mornings per week, with patient government and full-unit meetings filling this time slot on two other days. There are occupational and recreational therapy sessions every day of the week. There is a "patient report with nurses" every afternoon, and a staff conference for one hour on Monday through Friday afternoons. There is a weekly patient-staff "gripe meeting," a weekly field trip, a weekly meeting to discuss job finding, and a weekly community project meeting.

Initially each patient is expected to attend at least five times a week. As he improves, his schedule may be cut back to three or four days a week. All patients are expected to arrive on time, by 9:00 a.m., and to stay until 3:30 p.m.

Night patients are expected to arrive not later than six thirty at which time group therapy takes place three evenings a week. There are occupational therapy and recreational therapy sessions four evenings a week, a nurses' report six evenings a week, a dance on Friday evening, and a weekly unit meeting, "gripe meeting," and field trip. Patients are not allowed to go to bed until 10 p.m. but all of them are expected to be in bed by midnight. During those two hours they may watch television or socialize. Night patients are expected to attend at least six nights a week.

Evening patients participate in exactly the same program as night patients except that they do not sleep at the hospital. They are expected to remain on the premises until 10 p.m. and to have departed by midnight.

Medications. Patients who require medication during the time they are at the hospital receive them from the nurse. Patients who require medication while away from the hospital are given prescriptions. No one is permitted to bring medication with him to the hospital.

Work-for-pay. There is no such program as yet. This has a high priority in planning. The program hopes to develop job contacts and in-hospital contract work.

Job rehabilitation. The vocational skills of all patients are evaluated by the rehabilitation counselor. Patients who have no jobs can be placed in a sheltered workshop or a prevocational training program. For patients who appear to be able to work, jobs are obtained through the state's Division of Vocational Rehabilitation. At the weekly "job meeting" guidance is available about job hunting, and there is a postdischarge group, led by the Day and Night Center social workers, that focuses on work and work problems. Patients are also counseled individually by social service in regard to specific jobs and training, and social service acts as liaison between patient and specific employment agencies. There is at present a plan to use hospital jobs for training and for longer-term employment for suitable patients.

Boarding. Arrangements can be made for a patient to stay temporarily in the inpatient service or in the night hospital. This is usually done on medical grounds, but it has occasionally been done on a domiciliary basis. For patients who do not have suitable homes, a recommendation is sometimes made for them to move away from their relatives. Social service works individually with patients on problems of future living arrangements and helps them seek apartments or other appropriate places to live in New York City. Occasional placements have been arranged at an elaborate halfway house and rehabilitation center called Fountain House.

Disposition. For the last six months of 1967, 145 patients were separated from partial hospitalization status. About a quarter of these (24 percent), a rather high figure compared to other programs we visited, were transferred to the inpatient service. Forty-three percent were transferred to the outpatient service; 19 percent were referred to private physicians for further care; two percent were transferred to the inpatient service of other hospitals; and 12 percent left the partial hospitalization service against medical advice. This final figure accounts for a substantial portion of those whose stay in the program was two weeks or less.

Outcome. Studies evaluating the outcome of treatment in the partial hospitalization service had not been undertaken as of the time of our visit, but are now in progress. Figures on 155 discharges in 1967 indicated 91 as in remission or improved.

Transportation

The hospital is accessible by public transportation.

Agency relationships

The social workers work directly with the patients and family members to secure services from the Department of Social Services, homemaker agencies, schools, community centers, children's day care, health care, and other nonpsychiatric agencies. The staff have made visits to agencies of all types to acquaint them with the program and to work out ways to help them with their clients and ways in which the Day and Night Center can use agency facilities for their patients after discharge.

Financing

Mt. Sinai is a big city hospital with extremely high costs, so that only persons with high incomes can afford to meet the charges from their own funds. The principal health insurance policies will not cover the charges for partial hospitalization on day status. Perhaps most important, the regulations of the New York City Community Mental Health Board create a very great obstacle.

Like various other private general hospitals in New York City, Mt. Sinai provides contracted service to the city. The mental health board will not pay at all for evening or weekend patients; it will pay for night patients. It will pay for not more than ninety calendar days of treatment in the day hospital, under very restrictive terms. The patient must attend for at least five and one-half hours per day for at least three days per week in order to be covered at all, and if he does, a full seven days is charged against his ninety-day eligibility. In other words, a patient whose therapeutic needs indicate three visits per week may in fact attend the program only 39 days, while being tallied for 90 days. The hospital is paid only for the days that he actually attends. This arrangement explains in part why the program feels it necessary to operate seven days per week. It creates an arbitrary and artificial cutoff point at the three-day-per-week minimum, when certain patients might be better served by a gradual tapering off to two days and then one day per week. The hospital is trying hard to change this.

Future plans

Dr. Feder added that priority consideration will be given to the following:

1. Alter third-party financing arrangements to allow for greater flexibility in attendance, especially in the later stages of a patient's stay.

2. Change overall hospital policy to shift greater responsibility of the daily work requirements and housekeeping chores to the patients for therapeutic considerations.

3. Enlarge the rehabilitation program in work areas to include on-the-job training and to allow for paid contract work in the hospital. "Useful work-oriented activity has a tremendous therapeutic impact, as has been amply demonstrated at Fountain House," Dr. Feder said.

4. Develop the evening hospital. "There is greater demand for this than anything else," we were told. "Many patients who work or go to school would benefit by this without the need to stay overnight in the hospital."

5. Develop an apartment program, to be financed initially by the hospital, to be used for discharged patients without other places to live. Such patients would continue to have periodic contact with the hospital, would continue to receive assistance, and would take over the support of the apartment as soon as they were able. Fountain House has 20 to 25 such apartments throughout New York City.

6. Expand contact with local counseling services, community centers, activities groups, etc., as places for discharged patients to continue with their social and work rehabilitation.

Mt. Sinai was considering, at the time of our visit, applying for support as a community mental health center under the federal program. Assuming that federal funds would be available for new applicants, such a change in operation would probably ease, at least temporarily, the present strictures on partial hospitalization that result from the present financial situation.

Hahnemann Community Mental Health Center
Philadelphia

THE PSYCHIATRY DEPARTMENT of Hahnemann Medical College is integrated with a community mental health center. Having been established as a mental health center only in January 1967, the program had by the time of our visit in March 1968 already accomplished significant outreach into the community, providing services designed to meet the particular needs of its deprived catchment. The philosophical base of the program seemed to be still evolving. Specifically, the Hahnemann psychiatric program has been firmly grounded in dynamically oriented individual psychotherapy, whereas the deprived "urban ghetto" which it serves is populated with the kind of persons generally said to be unresponsive to and unsuitable for traditional individual psychotherapy. Since this situation is one likely to confront other teaching facilities, as mental health services increasingly attempt to meet the needs of the lower class, it will be of particular interest to observe how this particular community mental health center develops.

The inpatient service consists of a ward at Philadelphia General Hospital, centrally located in the city of Philadelphia, approximately a fifteen-minute drive from Hahnemann Medical College. The college itself, and the other components of the mental health center, are located in a deteriorated section of the inner city. The 170,000 population of the catchment is said to be the most deprived in Philadelphia. The majority are Negroes. There are many Puerto Ricans.

The day hospital, evening hospital, emergency service, and out-patient service are housed on the eleventh floor of a building that was formerly a commercial hotel. (All of the rest of the building is now occupied by an athletic club.) The program has ten community mental health workers, nine of them Negroes, all trained at the bachelor's level; certain of them are deployed to satellite operations—one each at a settlement house and at two churches that have community programs, and two at an information and referral center supported by a drug company.

162

Physical plant

The facilities in the former hotel were felt by the day hospital staff to provide adequate quarters. The space for patients is limited to a former corner suite, providing a dayroom, an occupational therapy room, and a nursing station. The former sleeping rooms of the hotel are used as staff offices.

Capacity and range of census

The stated capacity of the day hospital is 24 patients. From its opening in April 1967 through the end of that year the daily attendance ranged from eight to 26 persons. During a week in mid-January 1968 there were 17 persons who attended; 15 of these attended five days and one each attended three and four days. All except one came for the full day, from 9 a.m. to 4 p.m. On the day of our visit, in March 1968, there were 12 patients attending.

The staff

There were as many full-time staff members as patients at the time of our visit, and even when the program operates at its stated capacity there is one full-time staff member for each two patients in attendance. There is a substantial amount of additional time from personnel assigned part time to this program.

The day hospital, and indeed the entire community mental health center, suffered a sudden and extreme setback early in 1968 when its director, Dr. Morris Goldman, died of a heart attack. From all that we heard he appeared to have been a man who inspired exceptional devotion and great involvement; two months after his death the staff seemed still to be grieving for him. The day hospital and the inpatient service were being run under an interim arrangement whereby two staff psychiatrists, each working about three-quarters time, were designated the co-directors of both services. A new director had been recruited and was scheduled to take up his duties in mid-1968.

The full-time employees consisted of two psychiatric residents, five registered nurses, three aides, and two art therapists. The part-time employees consisted of two first-year residents, four second-year residents, a quarter-time psychologist, two half-time social workers, three community workers, six art therapists, and a movement therapist.

The richness of psychiatric staffing was accounted for by the emphasis on individual psychotherapy (described below). The richness of staffing in other categories appeared to be related to the fact that this is a teaching program. Day hospitals in most communities in this country will probably find it impossible to come even close to the staff-patient ratios of this program.

There had been no use of volunteers.

Referrals

Of 74 persons who were on day status during the nine months that the day hospital was open during 1967, 37, or exactly half, were referred by the mental health center's emergency service. Staffed around the clock, this service is located on the same floor as the day hospital. The examining psychiatrist determines what intensity of service is required by the person presented at the emergency room, and, interestingly, the service to which the person is assigned must accept him automatically. The staff of the receiving service may later decide to transfer or discharge him, but cannot refuse admission. We were told by the director of the emergency service that the criteria for assignment to the day hospital are these:

• Will the patient go?

• Is he sufficiently manageable that he can be treated without 24-hour supervision?

• Is it safe for him to go home?

• Does he have sufficient motivation and insight to accept his sickness and therefore his need for treatment in the day hospital?

The next largest group of patients accepted, 27 during 1967, or 36 percent, came from private psychiatrists. The remaining ten patients (14 percent of 1967 admissions) were divided among a) transfers from the outpatient clinic, b) self- and family referrals, and c) transfers from the state hospital.

The staff of the day hospital approached Philadelphia State Hospital, offering to accept up to twenty of their patients on transfer to the day hospital, but this effort was not successful; as of the time of our visit only two such patients had been transferred.

There had also been repeated efforts to persuade the reception center at Philadelphia General Hospital to refer Hahnemann catchment area patients to the day hospital, but with little success. This reception center is the major pathway in Philadelphia for persons considered to need treatment for serious mental illness. It may dispose of an individual patient by referring him to a ward of that hospital, to a state hospital, to some private hospital conducting a research program for which he is appropriate, to outpatient treatment, or to various other services.

The efforts of the community-based services in Philadelphia to have the reception center routinely refer to them patients from their catchment areas had not been very successful. During the first five months of 1968, a total of 26 persons living in the Hahnemann catchment area were sent by the reception center directly to Philadelphia State Hospital, despite the desire of the Hahnemann center to have all such persons referred to its own program.

Selection procedure

We have described above the characteristics looked for in patients being referred to the day hospital. The only persons who are categorically excluded are those who are actively suicidal or have organic brain syndromes.

Characteristics of the patients

The largest number of patients in terms of diagnosis are schizophrenics—19 persons, or 26 percent, during 1968. Other diagnoses were as follows:

Paranoid reactions	19%
Psychoneurotic disorders	12
Personality disorders	9
Stress and adjustment reactions	8
Alcoholism	8
Manic-depressive reactions	3
Others	15

About three fifths of the day patients (59 percent) were women.

At the time of our visit the social and economic characteristics of the day patients were more of the middle than the lower class, but we were told that at other times there have been a majority of lower-class patients. Certainly those we saw did not appear to us to be representative of the deprived population of the catchment area, and in this respect it is important to realize that while the Hahnemann Mental Health Center provides its services to all applicants who live within its catchment area, it also serves persons from outside the area. Such persons comprise a number of the referrals from psychiatrists in private practice, and this explains in part why the day patients are not entirely representative of the catchment area. A second reason seems to be related to the perception of the suitability of day hospitalization. Dr.

C. J. Bodarky, a psychologist who is executive officer for the center and was the acting director at the time of our visit, expressed the view that the day hospital might be more suitable for the middle-class patient, due to the lack of social supports for the lower-class patient; specifically, someone to care for the children at home and to provide evening and weekend support. He did not feel, however, that there was anything inherent in the pathology that made day treatment more suitable for the middle class.

Average length of stay for day patients during 1968 fell between 15 and 16 days of attendance.

Treatment philosophy

This day hospital is designed to furnish treatment to patients who need such intensive care that they would require 24-hour treatment were it not for the availability of an appropriate home to go to. The facility is viewed as providing everything that a hospital provides except a place to sleep. As a second and secondary function, it backs up the emergency service as a holding operation; that is, if a person seen in the emergency service needs immediate help, he can be seen briefly in the day hospital for evaluation, in the process avoiding admission as a 24-hour patient. The function of some day hospitals of providing maintenance care to nonacute patients who might otherwise be sent to state hospitals or other long-term facilities is not seen as a suitable role for this day hospital. An occasional person in this category has been referred to Horizon House, a large and elaborate rehabilitation residence located in Philadelphia. The center also inaugurated its own rehabilitation program in January 1968.

In pursuing what it is within the program that helps the patient, we explored particularly the attitudes toward formal individual psychotherapy, since this comprises a major emphasis. Many of the day patients are seen for three or four 50-minute interviews per week. One psychiatrist that we interviewed expressed the belief that individual psychotherapy accounted more than anything else for the patient's improvement; he said if asked to state the matter quantitatively, he would assign sixty percent of the beneficial effect to individual psychotherapy and forty percent to other components of the program. Another psychiatrist told us that he felt individual psychotherapy was principally an overlay on the group treatment program—that it existed largely to meet teaching needs and that the effect of the program on the patients would not be significantly different if individual psychotherapy were discontinued.

The treatment program

The central role of individual psychotherapy has been mentioned. The staff also see group interaction as therapeutic. No staff member referred to the day hospital as a therapeutic community, and it does not seem to be such in the sense of Maxwell Jones. There appeared, however, to be a therapeutic milieu, with most of the patients involved both in formal group therapy, three times per week, and also in various group activities.

The first hour of the day, at the time of our visit, was spent informally with the patients and staff joining together for coffee and conversation. That session has since been formalized into a daily milieu group. The rest of the morning is spent either in group therapy or in occupational therapy or games, depending on the day of the week. After lunch an hour and a half is scheduled for some activity either within the center or on the outside, again depending on the day of the week; examples are, on the outside, bowling, and on the inside, movement therapy. The patients then spend about half an hour cleaning up the dayroom and art rooms, then meet with the staff for the final half hour to discuss any pertinent developments of the day and to consider suggestions for future trips and activities.

Individual psychotherapy takes place primarily during the times when group activities are not scheduled. One-to-one relationships between patients and nursing personnel and art therapists take place throughout the day and are encouraged. The occupational therapy activities are incorporated into the art therapy; the chief art therapist, whom we interviewed, appeared to be a warm person who was well trained and who had a great deal of interest in the patients. She told us that the variety of art activities provided an outlet for substantially all of the patients, including those with little creative ability. Whenever a patient produces a seemingly significant art object, the therapist brings it to the attention of the doctor, although not in a highly symbolic and interpretive fashion.

Medication. Substantially all of the day patients receive psychotropic drugs. The day hospital staff obtain medication from the pharmacy and dispense it daily. For medication that the patient takes at home, prescriptions are provided. "This is a cumbersome procedure which we hope eventually to be able to change," we were told. "We try to encourage our patients as much as possible to take control of their own medication, both here and at home." Most of the patients are on light to medium dosage, regularly reviewed.

Work-for-pay. As of mid-1968, the day hospital was in process of setting up work-for-pay projects in collaboration with Hahnemann Hospital.

Boarding. Because there are no beds at the day hospital, an agitated day patient could be temporarily boarded only by transporting him to the Hahnemann service at Philadelphia General Hospital. This has rarely happened.

Late in 1968 a fourteen-bed inpatient unit became available at the Hahnemann Medical College Hospital, one block away from the day hospital, making it more feasible to board day patients temporarily.

Family involvement. Home visits are made on all day hospital patients by social workers and/or community mental health workers. In certain circumstances psychiatric residents and nurses make home visits; for example, if a patient fails to attend or if his family reports that he is seriously agitated at home. Two purposes are thus served by home visits: evaluation of the family structure and resources, and emergency help from the psychiatric staff for the agitated or reluctant patient. No family therapy as such was going on, but there were plans for residents to begin doing family evaluation interviews and for the staff to work with groups of families.

Disposition. Of 69 persons who were separated from day status during 1968, the largest group—27, or 39 percent—were transferred to the mental health center's outpatient service. Another nine (13 percent) were referred to another facility for outpatient follow-up, and an equal number were referred to private physicians for further care. Another nine left the program against medical advice. Seven, or ten percent, were transferred to inpatient status either within the Hahnemann program or elsewhere.

Outcome. The day hospital had been operating just under a year at the time of our visit. Studies evaluating the outcome of treatment had not been initiated.

Residential and job placements

Shortly after admission each patient's future disposition is considered, including an evaluation of his work history and an assessment of any vocational training and job placement service he may require. A few patients have started job training programs on a part-time basis while continuing to come to the day hospital on other days. An "aftercare rehabilitative service," established at the beginning of 1968, provides aftercare for day hospital patients.

Vocational counselors assigned to the day hospital participate in all intake and discharge staff conferences. In mid-1968 they were setting up with Hahnemann Hospital opportunities for day patients to work in various capacities within the general hospital.

In occasional instances supervised living arrangements have been made for patients whose living situation was inappropriate or undesirable.

Records

Two of the consultants examined a few records of day patients. These records were found to be exceptionally complete and of very high quality. Indications of concomitant physical illness seemed to have been detected even in obscure circumstances.

Transportation

We were told by various staff members that transportation has not been a significant problem. The day hospital, located on a main artery, is reasonably accessible by public transportation. Vouchers for taxicabs have been available for some patients who could not avail themselves of public transportation.

Financing

The cost of a day of care in the day hospital has been set at $20, although this appears to be an arbitrary figure rather than a true one that reflects all of the very rich professional time that is invested in this program. The charge covers all treatment and lunch. Only six percent of the patients pay the full charge; 36 percent pay a reduced charge; 58 percent pay nothing.

The program appears to be in good condition in terms of future financing. As part of a comprehensive community-based service, the day hospital will be entitled to reimbursement by the State of Pennsylvania up to the extent of ninety percent of its operating costs.

Future plans

Shortly after our visit, Dr. Robert J. Nathan became chief of the day hospital. He had partially reorganized the program, eliminating the "team" approach and assigning one assistant chief in charge of the day hospital and one for the fourteen-bed inpatient facility that was nearing completion. Each of these assistant chiefs in turn had a staff psychiatrist with whom he worked. Both of the services will begin to reorganize therapeutically along the lines of a milieu therapy ward (after Kenneth Artiss). This will involve much of the same program as at the time of our visit—daily milieu therapy meetings run by the assistant chiefs of the service and, where indicated, intensive small-group psychotherapy, plus art therapy and individual psychotherapy. Dr. Nathan expressed the hope that the autonomous day program and inpatient program could be coordinated sufficiently to really work as one unit totally sharing facilities. "A determined effort is currently being made to increase the census of the day hospital to the maximum attendance that the staff can handle," he said, "with special emphasis on patients from our catchment."

With the cooperation of the rehabilitation service and art therapy, assigned prevocational and vocational procedures were scheduled to be added for all patients appearing to need them.

Bronx State Hospital

Bronx, New York

B RONX STATE HOSPITAL, a new state hospital that opened in 1963, serves approximately two thirds of the residents of the Bronx. In December 1966 the first day hospital service was opened, with the support of a National Institute of Mental Health Hospital Improvement Project grant. At the time the grant application was drawn up the hospital was not unitized and the proposal was therefore based on the premise that the day hospital would serve patients from throughout Bronx State Hospital. Shortly after the day hospital began to operate, the hospital was unitized geographically, so that certain of the geographic services began to provide their own limited day hospital programs. A special "training unit" established a few months later also affected the day hospital, in that certain patients who would probably have been candidates for its program were placed in the training unit instead. The Hospital Improvement Project grant funds were withdrawn from the day hospital in February 1968 in order to be used for other purposes. The day hospital was closed shortly thereafter.

At the time of our visit, in February 1968, Bronx State Hospital was organized into three geographic and four specialty services. Two of the geographic units, those serving the Lincoln Hospital district and the Sound View-Throgs Neck district, relate to the community mental health centers that serve those areas. The Sound View-Throgs Neck Community Mental Health Center and a subdivision of the Lincoln Hospital Mental Health Services operate their own day hospitals (see pp. 45 and 91). The third geographic service, with 400 beds, serving the Jacobi section of the Bronx, and one portion of the Lincoln section with 240 beds, were therefore the only geographic units that referred their patients to the day hospital. The day hospital was counted as one of the four specialty services; the other three—geriatric, addictions, and training—rarely referred patients to the day hospital.

171

The physical plant

The Bronx State Hospital is a complex of several white brick buildings located on a rather barren tract adjacent to an industrial section of the East Bronx. The buildings themselves are new and clean but quite institutional and impersonal in appearance. The day hospital occupied a suite on the ground floor of one of the larger buildings. Its facilities included a combination dayroom-dining room, a nursing station where records were kept, an occupational therapy shop, several small group meeting rooms, a kitchen, seven offices and interviewing rooms, a small examining room, a drug and storage room, and a small outdoor area. The space was quite adequate for the size of the staff and the number of patients.

Capacity and range of census

The stated maximum capacity was given as 60, although the day hospital never reached that figure. During 1967 the census varied from 15 to 43 persons. During a week in mid-January 1968 there were 27 persons who attended, approximately half of them for the full five-day week. There were four additional patients who were considered active but who did not attend during that week for various personal reasons.

The staff

This day hospital was richly staffed for the size of its patient load. There were two psychiatrists, two psychologists, a social worker, a registered nurse, four aides, an occupational therapy aide, a psychology intern, a secretary, and a part-time social work student.

Dr. Walter Friedman, the director, came to the program following five years with the Westchester Square Day Hospital, now incorporated into the Sound View-Throgs Neck Mental Health Center. Most of the staff seemed to be highly experienced, with many years of service in psychiatric programs, but none of them had had specific prior experience in a day hospital. The staff began to be gathered in October 1966, prior to the hospital's opening in December. Over a period of several weeks Dr. Friedman gave the staff a series of training lectures. After the day hospital was open various members of the staff participated in various inservice training programs within Bronx State Hospital, although none of these had to do specifically with partial hospitalization services.

Volunteers were not used in the program.

Referrals

There were only two sources of referral—the inpatient wards of Bronx State Hospital and the emergency room at Jacobi Hospital. In the early months substantially all of the referrals were from within Bronx State. As the day hospital program came to be somewhat better known at Jacobi, the number of referrals from that hospital increased. During 1967 a total of 135 persons were admitted to the day hospital; 29 percent of these came from Jacobi, 71 percent from Bronx State.

Selection procedure

Like most other day hospitals a number of criteria were used to determine whether a candidate should be admitted. The following list of exclusions was furnished to us: *a)* geriatric patients with resistant families and/or ambulation problems; *b)* markedly regressed schizophrenic patients, especially those with major catatonic symptoms; *c)* drug addicts; *d)* severe alcoholics, with or without organic brain damage; *e)* certain depressed patients, and any other patients who seemed to pose a suicide risk; *f)* patients who posed a homicide risk; *g)* children under the age of sixteen.

It is interesting to note that the program had no requirement about the patient's living with a family that will support him. A number of solitary persons were in the program.

Characteristics of the patients

The majority of the patients had had previous hospitalizations for mental illness. A considerable number had very long histories of mental illness. Indeed, the staff felt there was some degree of resistance from patients precisely because the program was housed within a state mental hospital. "These are the patients who were exposed to state hospitals in the days of seclusion and restraint and mattresses on the floor," we were told. "They have a difficult time accepting the open facility, and they seem to wonder what we have up our sleeves along with our friendly and considerate attitude toward them."

Almost half of the patients (47 percent) were men; this rather high proportion, in comparison with most psychiatric programs, was thought to result from the fact that most of the referrals came from a state hospital inpatient service.

Eighty percent of the patients were between 21 and 65 years old. Eighteen percent were under 21, and only two percent were over 65.

By far the most common diagnosis was schizophrenic reaction (70 percent), followed by paranoid reaction (11 percent), psychoneurotic disorder (seven percent), and personality disorder (six percent).

The majority of the patients were thought to be of lower-middle class.

Treatment philosophy

The principal purpose of this day hospital was to provide continued care to persons who had been inpatients in Bronx State Hospital. This is continuity in the sense not of providing continued exposure to the same therapists but in the sense of having available an intermediate intensity of care that could help the improved but still impaired patient to spend his evenings and weekends in the community. Originally the day hospital was envisaged as also providing aftercare for patients from all of the general treatment wards; however, with the advent of the geographic unitization each geographic unit began to provide its own aftercare (or in the case of those units affiliated with mental health centers, to refer their patients there for aftercare).

Consequently, by the time we visited the program the aftercare being provided in the day hospital was limited primarily to patients who had actually been on day status in this specific day hospital. Some of these patients came to the day hospital during the daytime for follow-up appointments; others came on a stipulated evening, to be seen either individually or with some family member or in group therapy.

The foregoing is related to the day hospital's philosophy that mental illness is usually chronic and that the treating facility ought properly to be available to the patient at any time; that is, that release from hospital signals only the end of an episode of fairly intensive treatment, following which continued contact of some intensity is likely to be necessary over a long period of time.

There had evidently been no thought in this particular program of attempting to perform the function of obviating the need for inpatient treatment for the acutely ill patient.

The treatment program

Dr. Friedman and his associates viewed their program as a therapeutic community, which it appeared to the consultants to be.

The staff met each morning during the time the patients were assembling. Starting at nine thirty the patients were seen in small groups. Specifically, each patient was assigned to one of four groups having from six to eight patients and two to three staff members each. These small groups met in group therapy sessions for an hour each morning, followed by individual occupational therapy activities until lunch time. (Group occupational therapy activities were tried repeatedly, but with very limited success.) The staff persons assigned to these small groups were charged with primary responsibility to their particular patients throughout the day.

Afternoons were spent in a continuation of occupational therapy and recreational activities and occasional outings to bowling alleys and theaters.

The patients were scheduled to stay until four o'clock. A number of them, especially those with young children, left earlier.

Medication. Medications were prescribed by the two psychiatrists and were furnished to the patients from a supply kept on the ward. There was no charge. The majority of patients were on psychotropic medications.

Work-for-pay. There was no work-for-pay program on the day hospital service itself. A separate and relatively recent work-for-pay program serves the entire hospital. Because of limited capacity, very few of the day hospital patients were placed there.

Length of stay. For patients released from day status in 1967, the average stay was sixty calendar days.

Transportation

For many of the patients it was difficult to reach the program. Those who lived in the more distant parts of the area served by this day hospital were required to take three buses, with travel time up to two hours. Furthermore the bus fare came to $1.20 per day; this charge was usually met by the welfare department for those patients who were welfare clients.

Financing

A considerable portion of the expense of operating this day hospital was met from the NIMH grant. The balance was furnished by the state, as part of the budget for Bronx State Hospital.

Within the New York State system, day hospitals are considered to be outpatient facilities and therefore no charge is made to the patients treated in them.

Questionnaire to Facilities Providing Partial Hospitalization

1. What types of partial hospitalization program do you offer?

	Date of opening	Present capacity
day hospitalization	————	————
evening hospitalization	————	————
night hospitalization	————	————
weekend hospitalization	————	————

2. Is the length of time a patient may remain on partial hospitalization status limited either by custom or by hospital policy? __yes __no (If yes, what is the maximum time? __days)

3. What is your program's schedule?

	H O U R S		
Day	Day Hospital	Evening Hospital	Night Hospital
Monday	__to__	__to__	__to__
Tuesday	__to__	__to__	__to__
Wednesday	__to__	__to__	__to__
Thursday	__to__	__to__	__to__
Friday	__to__	__to__	__to__
Saturday	__to__	__to__	__to__
Sunday	__to__	__to__	__to__

4. In practice, what categories of patients are excluded from, or rarely admitted to, your partial hospitalization services?

5. Where do your partial hospitalization programs take place?
   On inpatient psychiatric wards __yes __no
   In the hospital, but separate from inpatient psychiatric wards
   __yes __no
   If "yes," describe facilities
   Outside of hospital physical plant __yes __no
   If "yes," describe location and facilities

177

6. Is it your belief that your partial hospitalization services are identified more with _____the inpatient service _____the outpatient service

7. Please indicate the kinds and numbers of staff persons participating in your partial hospitalization program.

	Full time	*Part time*	
	Number in program	Number in program	Total hours per week spent by part-time staff
Psychiatric residents	_____	_____	_____
Psychologists	_____	_____	_____
Social workers	_____	_____	_____
Registered nurses	_____	_____	_____
Licensed practical nurses	_____	_____	_____
Aides, attendants	_____	_____	_____
Recreational therapists	_____	_____	_____
Occupational therapists	_____	_____	_____
Others (specify:_____	_____	_____	_____
_____	_____	_____	_____
_____)	_____	_____	_____

8. How many salaried psychiatrists (*not* psychiatric residents) participate in partial hospitalization services?
   Number full time_____   Number part time_____
          Combined hours per week, part time_____
   Describe the extent, if any, to which psychiatrists contribute uncompensated time to the partial hospitalization services _____

9. Who has the ultimate medical responsibility for patients on partial hospitalization status?

10. Do you use the services of volunteers either individually or in an organized program in your partial hospitalization service?
    ____yes ____no
    If "yes," please estimate the number of hours of volunteer service per week at present. _____
    Describe the kinds of things they do, and your purpose in utilizing their services.

11. To what extent are the following available and used in your partial hospitalization therapeutic program? (Please check EVERY line.)

	For most or all patients	For some patients	For few or no patients	Typical length of session

**FORMAL SCHEDULED
INDIVIDUAL PSYCHOTHERAPY**

(*not* including ward rounds
and other brief contacts)

by patient's doctor	—	—	—	—	min.
by hospital-employed doctor	—	—	—	—	,,
by psychiatric resident	—	—	—	—	,,
by psychologist	—	—	—	—	,,
by psychiatric social worker	—	—	—	—	,,
by psychiatric nurse	—	—	—	—	,,
by other (specify: ____)	—	—	—	—	,,
_____	—	—	—	—	,,

GROUP PSYCHOTHERAPY
Conducted by:

psychiatrist	—	—	—	—	,,
psychiatric resident	—	—	—	—	,,
psychologist	—	—	—	—	,,
psychiatric social worker	—	—	—	—	,,
psychiatric nurse	—	—	—	—	,,
other (specify:____)	—	—	—	—	,,
_____	—	—	—	—	,,

PSYCHOTROPIC DRUGS	—	—	—
ELECTROSHOCK	—	—	—
PLANNED AND SUPER-VISED RECREATIONAL THERAPY	—	—	—
PLANNED AND SUPER-VISED OCCUPATIONAL THERAPY	—	—	—
FACTORY SUB-CONTRACT WORK	—	—	—
OTHER PAID EMPLOY-MENT	—	—	—
SOCIAL RETRAINING	—	—	—
FAMILY THERAPY	—	—	—
INDOKLON SHOCK	—	—	—
OTHER (SPECIFY:_____ _____)	—	—	—

12. Please provide in the space below a distribution of all partial hospitalization patients during the week of January 15, 1968.

DAY PATIENTS

	Less than three hours per day	Three to five hours per day	Six to eight hours per day	EVENING PATIENTS	NIGHT PATIENTS
One day per week	—	—	—	—	—
Two days per week	—	—	—	—	—
Three days per week	—	—	—	—	—
Four days per week	—	—	—	—	—
Five days per week	—	—	—	—	—
Six days per week	—	—	—	—	—
Seven days per week	—	—	—	—	—

13. Please describe the content of:
    a. A usual day in your day hospitalization service
    b. An evening in your evening hospitalization service
    c. A night in your night hospitalization service
    d. A weekend in your weekend hospitalization service

14. How many patients were on any kind of partial hospitalization status at any time during 1967? _____patients

    How many of these were: _____men

    _____women

    Of these patients, how many were:
    _____under 21 years old
    _____21 to 65 years old
    _____over 65 years old

    Of these patients, indicate the number with the following primary diagnoses:

    _____acute brain syndrome
    _____chronic brain syndrome
    _____schizophrenic reaction
    _____manic-depressive reaction
    _____paranoid reaction
    _____involutional psychotic reaction and psychotic depressive reaction
    _____mental deficiency

    _____stress and adjustment reaction
    _____psychophysiologic reaction
    _____psychoneurotic disorder
    _____personality disorder
    _____alcoholism not otherwise diagnosed
    _____drug addiction not otherwise diagnosed
    _____all others

15. What was the range of the daily census during 1967 in your day
    hospital program? from____to____persons
    Evening hospital program? from____to____persons
    Night hospital program? from____to____persons
    Weekend hospital program? from____to____persons

16. How many of your patients who were on any kind of partial hospitalization status at any time in 1967 were admitted to your partial hospitalization program?

    ____from your hospital's inpatient service

    ____on transfer from another hospital's inpatient service

17. In 1967, what were the principal sources of referral to your partial hospitalization program of patients who were *not* transferred from your own psychiatric inpatient service?

Referral source	*Number*
_____	_____
_____	_____
_____	_____

18. For those separated from partial hospitalization status during 1967, what was the average length of time on partial hospitalization status?

    Day hospital ____days
    Evening hospital ____evenings
    Night hospital ____nights
    Weekend hospital ____weekends

    Of patients separated from partial hospitalization status during 1967, how many were:

    ____transferred to inpatient status in your hospital
    ____transferred to inpatient status in another hospital

    (Of these, how many to ____a general hospital
    ____a state mental hospital
    ____a private psychiatric hospital
    ____a Veterans Administration hospital)

    ____released without provision for further treatment
    ____transferred to nursing homes or rest homes
    ____placed in foster homes
    ____transferred to outpatient status within your facility
    ____transferred to outpatient status in another facility
    ____referred to private physician for further care
    ____other (please describe)

19. For patients that you released from partial hospitalization status in 1967, how many were released as:

    _____in remission   _____deceased

    _____improved   _____other

    _____unimproved

    _____against medical advice   _____total released

20. What is the current charge to the patients on day hospital status

                                                        $_____per day

              Evening hospital status $_____per evening

              Night hospital status $_____per night

              Weekend hospital status $_____per weekend

Does this charge include:

    meals   __yes __no

    transportation   __yes __no

If individual psychotherapy is used, is the charge for it included above? __yes __no

If group psychotherapy is used, is the charge for it included above? __yes __no

21. What percentage pay   _____the full charge

                           _____a reduced charge

                           _____nothing

22. Describe the extent of your activity in arranging for vocational training, job placement, and other nonclinical and/or community services for partial hospitalization patients.

23. If you have a recent annual report containing any material relevant to your partial hospitalization services, please furnish six copies. Please also furnish six copies of any papers, brochures, and similar materials describing your partial hospitalization services.

24. Please furnish on a separate sheet any further information that you feel is necessary or useful in providing orientation to your partial hospitalization services.

25. Please add any comments.

Selected Bibliography on Partial Hospitalization

Compiled by Susan M. Urbania

BARNARD, R., "Achieving Optimum Use of the Day Hospital." *Mental Hospitals,* Vol. 12 (May, 1961), pp. 18-19.

BARTON, W. E., *Administration in Psychiatry.* Springfield, Illinois, Charles C. Thomas, 1962.

BARTON, W. E., *et al., Impressions of European Psychiatry.* Washington, D. C., American Psychiatric Association, 1961.

BENNETT, D. H., "British Day Hospitals," in R. Epps and L. Hanes, eds., *Day Care of Psychiatric Patients* (Springfield, Illinois, 1964), pp. 116-126.

BIERER, J., "Day Hospitals and Community Care." *Comprehensive Psychiatry,* Vol. 4 (December, 1963), pp. 381-386.

BIERER, J., "The Day Hospital: Therapy in a Guided Democracy." *Mental Hospitals,* Vol. 13 (May, 1962), pp. 246-252.

BOAG, T. J., "Further Developments in the Day Hospital." *American Journal of Psychiatry,* Vol. 116 (March, 1960), pp. 801-806.

BOAG, T. J., "The Day Hospital as a Therapeutic Community," in H. Denber, ed., *Research Conference on Therapeutic Community* (Springfield, Illinois, 1960), pp. 163-176.

BUTTS, H. F., "The Harlem Hospital Center Psychiatric Day Hospital: A Three-Year Evaluation." *Journal of the National Medical Association,* Vol. 59 (July, 1967), pp. 273-277.

BUTTS, H. F., "The Organization of a Psychiatric Day Hospital." *Journal of the National Medical Association,* Vol. 56 (September, 1964), pp. 381-389.

CAMERON, D. E., MacLean, R., and Moll, A. E., "The Day Hospital." *Mental Hospitals,* Vol. 9 (May, 1958), pp. 54-56.

CAMERON, D. E., "The Day Hospital," in A. E. Bennett, *et al., The Practice of Psychiatry in General Hospitals* (Berkeley and Los Angeles, 1956), pp. 134-150.

CAMERON, D. E., "The Day Hospital: Experimental Form of Hospitalization for Patients." *Modern Hospital,* Vol. 69 (September, 1947), pp. 60-62.

CANTON, R., and HAGEST, R., "Day Care as a Substitute for Inpatient Care." *American Journal of Orthopsychiatry,* Vol. 32 (March, 1962), pp. 227-228.

CARMICHAEL, D. M., "Day Hospital Program with Emphasis on Translatable Skills," in R. Epps and L. Hanes, eds., *Day Care of Psychiatric Patients* (Springfield, Illinois, 1964), pp. 66-78.

CARMICHAEL, D. M., "A Psychiatric Day Hospital for Convalescent Patients." *Mental Hospitals,* Vol. 11 (January, 1960), pp. 7-8.

CHASIN, R., "Special Clinical Problems in Day Hospitalization." *American Journal of Psychiatry,* Vol. 123 (January, 1967), pp. 779-784.

COHEN, F., "The Psychiatric Day Hospital: I. A Low-Cost Day Program." *Mental Hospitals,* Vol. 16 (July, 1965), pp. 191-193.

COHEN, R., "Patient-Oriented Administration in a Day Hospital." *Mental Hospitals,* Vol. 11 (December, 1960), pp. 22-24.

COLMAN, A., and GREENBLATT, M., "Take Up Thy Bed and Walk." *Mental Hospitals,* Vol. 13 (May, 1962), pp. 268-270.

CONWELL, M., et al., "The First National Survey of Psychiatric Day-Night Services," in R. Epps and L. Hanes, eds., Day Care of Psychiatric Patients (Springfield, Illinois, 1964), pp. 106-115.

COWEN, J., and GOLDBERG, S., "The VA Day Center: A Design for Rehabilitation." Mental Hospitals, Vol. 13 (May, 1962), pp. 266-267.

CRAFT, M., "Psychiatric Day Hospitals." American Journal of Psychiatry, Vol. 116 (September, 1959), pp. 251-254.

CUMMING, J., "Day Hospital and Community Needs," in R. Epps and L. Hanes, eds., Day Care of Psychiatric Patients (Springfield, Illinois, 1964), pp. 127-140.

DANIELS, R. S., "Therapy in Day and Night Psychiatric Hospitals," in J. H. Masserman, ed., Current Psychiatric Therapies, Vol. 4 (New York and London, 1964), pp. 191-198.

DANIELS, R. S., "Issues in the Origin, Organization, and Operation of a Day Hospital," in R. Epps and L. Hanes, eds., Day Care of Psychiatric Patients (Springfield, Illinois, 1964), pp. 20-34.

DAVIES, I., ELLENSON, G., and YOUNG, R., "Therapy with a Group of Families in a Psychiatric Day Center." American Journal of Orthopsychiatry, Vol. 36 (January, 1966), pp. 134-146.

DE MARNEFFE, F., and PREKUP, J. T., "The McLean Hospital Rehabilitation Center." Mental Hospitals, Vol. 13 (August, 1962), pp. 410-413.

DINGMAN, P., "Day Hospitals for Children," in R. Epps and L. Hanes, eds., Day Care of Psychiatric Patients (Springfield, Illinois, 1964), pp. 53-65.

EWALT, J., ALEXANDER, G., and GRINSPOON, L., "Changing Practices: A Plea and Some Predictions." Mental Hospitals, Vol. 11 (June, 1960), pp. 9-13.

FARNDALE, J., The Day Hospital Movement in Great Britain. New York, Pergamon Press, 1961.

FREEDMAN, A., "Day Hospital for Severely Disturbed Schizophrenic Children." American Journal of Psychiatry, Vol. 115 (April, 1959), pp. 893-898.

FREEMAN, P., "Treatment of Chronic Schizophrenia in a Day Center." Archives of General Psychiatry, Vol. 7 (October, 1962), pp. 259-265.

GREENBLATT, M., "Day Hospital and the Therapeutic Society Ideal," in R. Epps and L. Hanes, eds., Day Care of Psychiatric Patients (Springfield, Illinois, 1964), pp. 3-19.

GRINSPOON, L., et al., "A Day Care Program on an Inpatient Service." Mental Hospitals, Vol. 14 (May, 1963), pp. 259-264.

GRINSPOON, L., and COHEN, R., "Introduction of a Part-Time Hospitalization Program into an Acute Psychiatric Treatment Service." The New England Journal of Medicine, Vol. 267 (October 11, 1962), pp. 752-756.

GUSSEN, J., "An Experimental Day-Night Hospital." Mental Hospitals, Vol. 11 (June, 1960), pp. 26-29.

GUY, W., and GROSS, G., "Problems in the Evaluation of Day Hospitals." Community Mental Health Journal, Vol. 3 (Summer, 1967), pp. 111-118.

HANES, L., and CURTIS, B., "The Day Hospital as a Staff-Patient Community," in R. Epps and L. Hanes, eds., Day Care of Psychiatric Patients (Springfield, Illinois, 1964), pp. 35-52.

HAYMAN, M., "Unique Day Therapy Center for Psychiatric Patients." Mental Hygiene, Vol. 41 (April, 1957), pp. 245-249.

HOGARTY, G., et al., "Who Goes There?—A Critical Evaluation of Admissions to a Psychiatric Day Hospital." American Journal of Psychiatry, Vol. 124 (January, 1968), pp. 934-944.

HUNTLEY, A. C., "The Psychiatric Day Hospital: II. A Day Program in Treatment and Teaching." Mental Hospitals, Vol. 16 (July, 1965), pp. 194-196.

JONES, A., CORMACK, G., and BOW, L., "Whither the Day Hospital." American Journal of Psychiatry, Vol. 119 (April, 1963), pp. 973-977.

JONES, C., "A Day Care Program for Adolescents in a Private Hospital." *Mental Hospitals,* Vol. 12 (October, 1961), pp. 4-6.

KEETON, J. E., "Goals and Pitfalls of Day Treatment Programs." *Mental Hospitals,* Vol. 15 (November, 1964), pp. 640-643.

KINDER, E., and DANIELS, R. S., "Day and Night Psychiatric Treatment Centers: Description, Organization, and Function." *American Journal of Psychiatry,* Vol. 119 (November, 1962), pp. 415-420.

KIRKPATRICK, W., "A Dual-Purpose Treatment Center: A Combination Day Hospital and Outpatient Clinic Serves Community Needs." *Mental Hospitals,* Vol. 10 (April, 1959), pp. 16-17.

KRAFT, A., "Day Hospital Services as Part of an Integrated Psychiatric Treatment Program," in R. Epps and L. Hanes, eds., *Day Care of Psychiatric Patients* (Springfield, Illinois, 1964), pp. 79-90.

KRAFT, A., "A Combined Full-Time and Part-Time Program." *Mental Hospitals,* Vol. 14 (July, 1963), p. 376.

KRAMER, B. M., "The Day Hospital as an Element in Comprehensive Psychiatry." *Mental Hospitals,* Vol. 14 (March, 1963), pp. 170-171.

KRAMER, B. M., *Day Hospital—A Study of Partial Hospitalization in Psychiatry.* New York, Grune and Stratton, 1962.

KRAMER, B. M., "The Day Hospital, The Community, and The Psychiatric Patient," in M. Greenblatt, *et al.,* eds., *Mental Patients in Transition* (Springfield, Illinois, 1961), pp. 72-75.

KRIS, E., "Day Hospitals." *Current Therapies Research,* Vol. 7 (May, 1965), pp. 320-323.

KRIS, E., "Prevention of Rehospitalization Through Relapse Control in a Day Hospital," in M. Greenblatt, *et al.,* eds., *Mental Patients in Transition* (Springfield, Illinois, 1961), pp. 155-162.

KRIS, E., "Intensive Short-Term Treatment in a Day Care Facility for the Prevention of Rehospitalization of Patients in the Community Showing Recurrence of Psychotic Symptoms." *Psychiatric Quarterly,* Vol. 34 (January, 1960), pp. 83-88.

LAMB, H. R., "Chronic Psychiatric Patients in the Day Hospital." *Archives of General Psychiatry,* Vol. 17 (November, 1967), pp. 615-621.

LANGSLEY, D. G., STEPHENSON, W., and MACDONALD, J., "Why Not Insure Partial Hospitalization." *Mental Hospitals,* Vol. 15 (January, 1964), pp. 16-17.

LAW, M., "All Therapeutic Activities Available to Day Patients." *Mental Hospitals,* Vol. 4 (February, 1953), p. 7.

LYSTAD, M., "Day Hospital Care and Changing Family Attitudes Towards the Mentally Ill." *Journal of Nervous and Mental Disease,* Vol. 127 (August, 1958), pp. 145-152.

MARGOLIS, P., "The Varied Uses of Part-Time Treatment." *Mental Hospitals,* Vol. 15 (October, 1964), pp. 574-579.

MARLER, D. C., "A Follow-up Study of a Weekend Hospital Program." *Mental Hospitals,* Vol. 15 (April, 1964), p. 204.

McDONOUGH, L., and DOWNING, J., "The Day Center as an Alternative to the Psychiatric Ward." *Mental Hygiene,* Vol. 49 (April, 1965), pp. 260-264.

McMILLAN, T., and AASE, B., "Analysis of First 500 Patients at San Diego Day Treatment Center," in R. Epps and L. Hanes, eds., *Day Care of Psychiatric Patients* (Springfield, Illinois, 1964), pp. 91-105.

MELTZOFF, J., and BLUMENTHAL, R. L., *The Day Treatment Center,* Springfield, Illinois, Charles C. Thomas, 1966.

MELTZOFF, J., and RICHMAN, A., "Therapeutic Rationale of a Psychiatric Day Center." *Psychiatric Quarterly,* Vol. 35 (April, 1961), pp. 295-305.

MOLL, A. E., *et al.,* "Part-Time Hospitalization." *Mental Hospitals,* Vol. 14 (February, 1963), pp. 123-124.

MOLL, A. E., "Night and Day Psychiatric Treatment Units in a General Hospital," in L. Linn, ed., *Frontiers in General Hospital Psychiatry* (New York, 1961), pp. 111-131.

MOLL, A. E., "Psychiatric Night Treatment Unit in a General Hospital." *American Journal of Psychiatry,* Vol. 113 (February, 1957), pp. 722-727.

MORGENSTERN, J., and UNGERLEIDER, J. T., "Integration of a Day-Care Program into a General Psychiatric Hospital." *American Journal of Psychiatry,* Vol. 122 (April, 1966), pp. 1178-1181.

NAKAJIMA, J., and ISHII, T., "A Night Hospital in Tokyo." *Hospital and Community Psychiatry,* Vol. 18 (April, 1967), pp. 104-105.

ODENHEIMER, J. F., "Day Hospital as an Alternative to the Psychiatric Ward: Attitudes and Responses of Relatives." *Archives of General Psychiatry,* Vol. 13 (July, 1965), pp. 46-53.

OLDHAM, A., "Psychiatric Day Treatment in the General Hospital." *International Journal of Social Psychiatry,* Vol. 12 (Spring, 1966), pp. 109-113.

PECK, H., "The Role of the Psychiatric Day Hospital in a Community Mental Health Program: A Group Process Approach." *American Journal of Orthopsychiatry,* Vol. 32 (March, 1962), pp. 229-230.

PFAUTZ, H., "The Functions of Day Care for Disturbed Adolescents." *Mental Hygiene,* Vol. 46 (April, 1962), pp. 223-229.

Proceedings of the 1958 Day Hospital Conference, Washington, D. C., American Psychiatric Association, 1958.

RICKELMAN, B., "Some Problems of Day Hospitals in Community Care of the Mentally Ill." *Community Mental Health Journal,* Vol. 4 (October, 1968), pp. 425-433.

RUBIN, E., "The Lafayette Clinic's Broad-Scale Rehabilitation Service." *Mental Hospitals,* Vol. 14 (July, 1963), pp. 383-385.

SILVERMAN, M., "Community Attitudes to Psychiatric Day Care." *International Journal of Social Psychiatry,* Vol. 13 (Winter, 1966), pp. 67-70.

SMITH, S., and CROSS, E., "Review of 1000 Patients Treated at a Psychiatric Day Hospital." *International Journal of Social Psychiatry,* Vol. 2 (Spring, 1957), pp. 292-298.

STEINMAN, L., and HUNT, R., "Day Hospital Treatment of Acute Psychiatric Illness," in J. H. Masserman, ed., *Current Psychiatric Therapies,* Vol. 2 (New York and London, 1962), pp. 196-199.

TANNENBAUM, G., PINSKER, H., and SAGER, C. J., "The Shoestring Day Hospital." *American Journal of Orthopsychiatry,* Vol. 35 (July, 1965), pp. 729-732.

TOBIN, J., and SMITH, J., "The Day Unit of New Jersey State Hospital, Trenton." *Mental Hospitals,* Vol. 7 (December, 1956), pp. 20-21.

VERNALLIS, F., and REINERT, R., "Group Treatment Methods in a Weekend Hospital." *Psychotherapy: Theory, Research, and Practice,* Vol. 3 (May, 1966), pp. 91-93.

VERNALLIS, F., and REINERT, R., "The Weekend Hospital." *Mental Hospitals,* Vol. 14 (May, 1963), pp. 254-258.

WEINER, D., "Problems and Directions for the Day Treatment Center." *Mental Hygiene,* Vol. 47 (July, 1963), pp. 411-417.

WEINSTEIN, G., "Objectives of VA Day Care Centers: The Volunteers' Contributions." *Mental Hospitals,* Vol. 15 (April, 1964), pp. 216-219.

WEINSTEIN, G., "Pilot Programs in Day Care." *Mental Hospitals,* Vol. 11 (January, 1960), pp. 9-11.

WHITE, G., "Members of the Club." *SK&F Psychiatric Reporter,* Vol. 17 (November-December, 1964), pp. 7-8.

WILDER, J., LEVIN, G., and ZWERLING, I., "A Two-Year Follow-up Evaluation of Acute Psychotic Patients Treated in a Day Hospital." *American Journal of Psychiatry,* Vol. 122 (April, 1966), pp. 1095-1101.

ZEMLICK, M., and MCMILLAN, T., "Day Treatment—A Study of a Year's Operation." *American Journal of Orthopsychiatry*, Vol. 32 (March, 1962), pp. 228-229.

ZWERLING, I., and WILDER, J., "An Evaluation of the Applicability of the Day Hospital in Treatment of Acutely Disturbed Patients." *Israel Annals of Psychiatry and Related Disciplines*, Vol. 2 (October, 1964), pp. 162-185.